JEPPESEN
MAINTENANCE
Mastery Realized.

A&P TECHNICIAN
AIRFRAME
STUDENT WORKBOOK

JEPPESEN®

Support Materials

Look for these support materials to complement your A&P Technician Airframe Workbook:

- **A&P Technician Airframe Textbook**
- **A&P Technician Airframe Study Guide**
- **Federal Aviation Regulations**
- **AC 43.13-1B/2A Acceptable Methods, Techniques and Practices/Aircraft Alterations**
- **Aircraft Technical Dictionary**
- **Standard Aviation Maintenance Handbook**

These items are among the wide variety of Jeppesen reference materials available through your authorized Jeppesen Dealer. If there is no Jeppesen Dealer in your area, you can contact us directly:

Jeppesen Sanderson
Sanderson Training Systems
55 Inverness Drive East
Englewood, CO 80112-5498
www.jeppesen.com

JS322711-000

PREFACE

The *A&P Technician Airframe Workbook* is designed to help you check your understanding of the material you studied in the A&P Technician Textbook. Each exercise is correlated with a specific textbook chapter and section. The workbook contains multiple choice, true/false, matching, and completion exercises. To answer the multiple choice questions, circle the letter of the correct choice. Fill in the appropriate blanks to answer the other questions. Further instructions are provided, when necessary. The answers to all of the exercises are grouped in the Answer Section at the back of this book.

TABLE OF CONTENTS

AIRCRAFT STRUCTURAL ASSEMBLY AND RIGGING

SECTION A
AIRCRAFT DESIGN AND CONSTRUCTION

1. Early airplanes usually used a _____ structure.

2. A(n) _____ (what type) structure carries all of the structural loads in its skin and is referred to as a _____ design.

3. The most common structural design for modern aircraft is a _____ structure where the skin, bulkheads, formers, stringers and other components carry the aerodynamic loads.

4. A(n) _____ (what type) fuselage has a substructure to stiffen the external skin.

5. A structure that is built with more than one path for the stresses so a crack will not destroy the structure is called a(n) _____ design.

6. The angle formed between the chord of the wing and the relative wind is known as the angle of _____.

7. Air passing across an airfoil will create a region of _____ (low or high) pressure above the airfoil.

8. What component attaches to the spars to give the wing the aerodynamic shape it needs to produce lift?
_____

9. The center of lift of an aircraft is usually located _____ (ahead or behind) the center of gravity.

10. Fabric-covered airplane wings usually have a(n) _____-type structure.

11. The steel wire that runs from the front spar inboard to the rear spar outboard in a truss-type wing is called a(n) _____ wire.

12. A wing which uses no external struts or braces for support is called a(n) _____ wing.

13. Milled skins for high-speed aircraft may be produced by conventional machining or by _____

    milling, or by _____ machining.

14. Laminated materials such as bonded honeycomb are used for aircraft structure because they provide maximum

    _____ as well as a favorable strength to weight ratio.

15. Control surfaces are balanced so that their center of gravity is _____ (ahead of or behind) the

    hinge line.

16. Stiffness of the thin sheet metal covering for a control surface may be increased by _____ the

    metal skin.

17. The three primary controls of an airplane are:

    a. _____

    b. _____

    c. _____

18. On jet transport aircraft equipped with two sets of ailerons, only the _____ (inboard or

    outboard) aileron is used during high-speed flight.

19. A(n) _____ is a control device that destroys lift by disrupting the airflow over a part of the wing.

20. The primary purpose of a winglet is to improve _____ by reducing _____ by diffusing

    the _____ _____.

21. _____ _____ (what unit) are pairs of small, low aspect ratio airfoil sections mounted on

    the upper surface of a wing to pull high-energy air down onto the surface to prevent shock-induced separation.

22. The assembly of tail surfaces of an airplane is called the _____.

23. The extension of the vertical stabilizer that may extend nearly to the cabin section is known as a(n)

    _____ fin.

24. An all movable horizontal tail surface is called a(n) _____.

25. An all-movable tail surface usually has a large tab installed on its trailing edge. This is known as a(n)

    _____ (servo or anti-servo) tab.

26. The movable surfaces on a V-tail design are known as _____.

27. The wings, tail, engine and landing gear are attached to the body of an aircraft, which is called the

    _____.

28. In a _____ (Pratt or Warren) truss fuselage, the stays carry only the tensile loads.

29. Both tensile and compressive loads are carried in the diagonal members of a _____ (Pratt or Warren) truss fuselage.

30. Aircraft using a tailwheel type landing gear configuration are also called _____ gear airplanes.

31. Aircraft using a nosewheel type landing gear configuration are also called _____ gear airplanes.

32. When a landing gear is retracted into the structure, the _____ (parasite or induced) drag is reduced.

33. Today, almost all piston-powered airplanes enclose the engine in a(n) _____ cowling.

34. Heat is removed from the cylinders of an air-cooled engine by forcing air to flow through _____ on the cylinders.

35. The amount of airflow through the fins of a high-powered engine is usually controlled by _____ _____ at the air exit.

36. Cowl flaps are normally _____ (open or closed) during ground operations.

37. The two most common locations for turbojet or turbofan engine installations are:

    a. _____

    b. _____

SECTION B
AIRPLANE ASSEMBLY AND RIGGING

1. The three axes of an airplane are:

    a. _____ or _____

    b. _____ or _____

    c. _____ or _____

2. The ailerons rotate an airplane about its _____ axis.

3. The elevators rotate an airplane about its _____ axis.

4. The rudder will rotate an aircraft about its _____ axis.

5. The _____ is used to overcome the effects of aileron drag.

6. The two types of stability exhibited by an aircraft are:

    a. _____

    b. _____

7. About which of the three axes of an airplane do each of these items provide stability:

    a. Horizontal tail surfaces: _____

    b. Dihedral in the wing: _____

    c. Vertical fin on the tail: _____

8. The fixed horizontal tail surface is called the horizontal _____.

9. The movable horizontal tail surfaces are called the _____.

10. The tail load of an airplane in level flight normally acts _____ (upward or downward).

11. When the control wheel of the aircraft is pulled back, the trailing edge of the elevator moves

    _____ (up or down).

12. An elevator downspring is used to provide a mechanical force on the elevators as a safety factor when the airplane is

    flown with its center of gravity near its _____ (forward or rearward) limit.

13. If a pilot pushes the control yoke forward, the trailing edge of a stabilator will move _____ (up or down)

14. To bank an airplane to the right, the aileron on the right wing moves _____ (up or down).

15. The two aileron bellcranks are connected by a _____ cable.

16. The temporary movement of the nose of an airplane toward the wing that is rising at the beginning of a turn is caused

    by _____.

17. Which aileron travels a greater distance, the one moving up or the one moving down? The one moving

    _____ (up or down).

18. A(n) _____ -type aileron has its hinge line located far enough back that its leading edge will

    protrude below the wing surface when the aileron is raised.

19. Many airplanes use rudder-aileron _____ _____ to compensate for aileron drag.

20. Depressing the right rudder pedal will move the trailing edge of the rudder to the _____ (right

    or left

21. A(n) _____ is usually mounted on a control surface to correct for an out-of-trim condition.

22. A balance tab moves in the _____ (same or opposite) direction as the control surface to which

    it is attached.

23. Stabilators are normally equipped with _____(servo or anti-servo) tabs.

24. An anti-servo tab moves in the _____(same or opposite) direction as the control surface to which it is attached.

25. A servo tab moves in the _____ (same or opposite) direction as the control surface to which it is attached.

26. A spring tab moves only when the control forces are _____ (high or low).

27. Large airplanes, which utilize an adjustable stabilizer, move the leading edge of the stabilizer up or down by means of a _____.

28. Moving the leading edge of an adjustable stabilizer up, trims the airplane nose-_____(up or down).

29. When wing flaps are lowered, they increase both the lift and the _____ that is produced by the wing.

30. When plain flaps are lowered, they _____ (increase or decrease) the camber of the wing.

31. _____ (what type) flaps are used to prevent the airflow from breaking away from the upper surfaces when the flaps are fully extended.

32. A(n) _____ (what type) flap rides out of the trailing edge of the wing on tracks and increases the wing area as well as its camber.

33. A fixed _____(slot or slat) ducts air over the top of the wing to keep the _____ (aileron or flap) effective and provide lateral control during most of a stall.

34. Leading edge slats may be extended by one of two methods. What are these methods?

    a. _____

    b. _____

35. A leading edge flap increases the _____ of the wing.

36. Ideally, a wing should first stall at the _____(root or tip).

37. A stall strip is a small triangular strip of metal or rubber installed on the leading edge of a wing _____ (at the wing root or ahead of the aileron).

38. The difference in pressure between the lower and upper surfaces of a wing causes air to spill over the wing tip and creates wing tip _____.

39. Wing tip vortices create drag and reduce lift, especially at _____ (high or low) angles of attack and _____ (high or low) airspeeds.

40. _____ are a popular method of controlling wing tip vortices on modern, high-speed aircraft.

41. A _____ _____ is a simple method to stop, or reduce, the spanwise flow of air on a wing.

42. A lifting surface located at the front of an airplane that replaces a conventional horizontal stabilizer is called a _____.

43. Hydraulically boosted control systems use _____ (reversible or irreversible) inputs to prevent control surface buffeting from being fed back to the pilot.

44. Two types of devices used by the Boeing 747 for lateral control are:

    a. _____

    b. _____

45. The Boeing 747 has _____(how many) independent rudders to provide yaw control.

46. Dutch roll is prevented in the Boeing 747 by the use of a(n) _____ _____.

47. What two devices, other than the triple-slotted Fowler flaps, alter the camber of a Boeing 747 wing when the flaps are lowered?

    a. _____

    b. _____

48. Control surface travel specifications for a particular make and model of aircraft may be found in what FAA publication? _____

49. A wing is said to be _____(washed-in or washed-out) if it is rigged to reduce its angle of incidence and decrease its lift.

50. Some aircraft aileron systems are rigged so that when there is no airload both ailerons will be a few degrees below the trailing edge of the wing. This is known as aileron _____.

51. Fill in the strand number designation for each of these cable types:

    a. Non-flexible _____ or _____

    b. Flexible _____

    c. Extra-flexible _____

52. What percentage of the full cable strength may be obtained with each of these terminations?

    a. Woven splice _____%

    b. Nicopress sleeve _____%

53. After installing the terminals on a control cable, it should be subjected to a proof load test, which is

_____ (what percent) of the breaking strength of the cable.

54. Aircraft control cables should be carefully checked for what two defects?

    a. _____

    b. _____

55. Fairleads _____(may or may not) be used to change the direction of a cable.

56. Using the cable tension chart in Figure 1-86 of the *Jeppesen A&P Technician Airframe Text*, find the correct tension

for the following conditions:

    a. 3/16-inch 7X19 cable when adjusted at 40 degrees Fahrenheit = _____ pounds

    b. 1/8-inch 7X19 cable when adjusted at 40 degrees Fahrenheit = _____ pounds

    c. 1/8-inch 7X19 cable when adjusted at 90 degrees Fahrenheit = _____ pounds

    d. 1/16-inch 7X7 cable when adjusted at 70 degrees Fahrenheit = _____ pounds

57. For a turnbuckle to develop its full strength, there must be no more than _____(how many)

threads exposed at either end of the barrel.

58. When safety-wiring a turnbuckle, you should have at least _____(how many) full wraps of

wire around the shank before the wire is cut off.

59. When installing threaded rod end fittings for push-pull type controls, if you can pass a piece of safety wire through the

check hole, the rod end _____ (is or is not) screwed in far enough.

60. When the upper wing of a biplane is ahead of the lower wing, the airplane is said to have

_____(positive or negative) stagger.

61. The difference between the angle of incidence between the two wings of a biplane is known as

_____.

62. The streamlined wires on a biplane that run from the center section to the interplane strut on the lower wing are called

the _____(flying or landing) wires.

63. When assembling a biplane, the _____(upper or lower) wing panels are installed first.

64. A _____ is completed when a jet transport takes off, is pressurized, then depressurizes and lands.

65. The structure of jet transports may become weakened over time by:

    a. _____

    b. _____

66. After a transport aircraft has been in service for a specified number of years or has accumulated a certain number of

    cycles, it must undergo a series of _____ and _____ as part of the _____

    _____ _____.

SECTION C
FUNDAMENTALS OF ROTARY-WING AIRCRAFT

1. The rotor of an autogiro is turned by _____ forces.

2. Torque of the main rotor is compensated on a single-rotor helicopter by the use of a(n)

    _____.

3. Two ways of counteracting torque from a dual-rotor helicopter system are:

    a. _____

    b. _____

4. Rigid rotor systems have movement only about their _____(flap, drag, or feather) axis.

5. The four forces acting on a helicopter rotor are:

    a. _____

    b. _____

    c. _____

    d. _____

6. Most helicopters use a(n) _____(symmetrical or asymmetrical) airfoil section.

7. What are the two gyroscopic forces that act on the spinning rotor of a helicopter?

    a. _____

    b. _____

8. _____(precession or coriolis effect) causes the rotor to tilt 90 degrees away from the point the

    control force is applied.

9. _____(precession or coriolis effect) causes a rotor blade to attempt to speed up as it flaps up and moves its center of mass closer to the rotor mast.

10. Coriolis effect is minimized on a semi-rigid rotor by using an _____(underslung or offset) hub.

11. Ground effect is normally considered to extend upward from the surface about _____(what portion) of a rotor span.

12. What is meant by the abbreviation OGE? _____

13. What is meant by the abbreviation IGE? _____

14. The helicopter blade that moves in the same direction that the helicopter is moving is called the _____(advancing or retreating) blade.

15. A helicopter experiences dissymetry of lift during _____(hovering or forward) flight.

16. Dissymetry of lift is compensated for by blade _____ and _____.

17. A helicopter rotor normally stalls on the _____(advancing or retreating) blade.

18. A helicopter rotor stalls in _____(high- or low-) speed flight.

19. Lift produced by a helicopter rotor system because of forward flight is called _____lift.

20. If a helicopter experiences engine failure, the rotor is turned by an aerodynamic force known as the _____ force.

21. During powered flight airflow through the rotor is _____(upward or downward).

22. During autorotation, the airflow through the rotor of a helicopter is _____(upward or downward).

23. The helicopter control that changes the pitch on all the rotor blades at the same time is called the _____ pitch control.

24. In order to maintain a constant rotor R.P.M, engine power must be changed every time the pitch of the rotor blades changes. Two mechanisms used to accomplish these power changes are the _____ and the _____.

25. On most helicopters, the throttle consists of a twist-grip mounted on the end of the _____ (cyclic or collective) control.

26. The helicopter control that changes the pitch of the rotor blades at a certain point in their rotation is called the _____ pitch control.

27. The fuselage of some helicopters is kept relatively level in flight at high airspeed by using a(n)

    _____ _____ controlled by the cylic pitch control to increase the down

    load on the tail as the cyclic control is moved forward.

28. Boosted controls on a helicopter cannot feed vibration back through the controls if an _____

    control system is used.

29. The pitch of the tail rotor is controlled by _____ operated by the pilot.

30. A tail rotor located within a circular duct is called a _____.

31. A helicopter is inherently _____(stable or unstable).

32. Three systems used to increase the stability of a helicopter are:

    a. _____

    b. _____

    c. _____

33. Low frequency vibration is felt as a(n) _____(beat or buzz).

34. Vibrations caused by the main rotor system are usually of the _____(low or high) frequency

    type.

35. An out-of-track rotor would normally cause a _____(lateral or vertical) vibration.

36. An out-of-balance rotor would normally cause a _____(lateral or vertical) vibration.

37. Helicopter blades must be balanced both:

    a. _____

    b. _____

38. Helicopter blades are also balanced in two directions. These are:

    a. _____.

    b. _____.

39. Three methods of checking main rotor blade track are:

    a. _____

    b. _____

    c. _____

40. Adjusting the length of the pitch change rods is normally done to correct an out-of-track condition found

    _____(on the ground or in flight).

41. Bending the rotor blade trim tabs is normally done to correct an out-of-track condition found

    _____(on the ground or in flight).

42. Cooling air is supplied to a reciprocating engine installed in a helicopter by a(n) _____.

43. Helicopter power output is controlled by the _____ pitch control.

44. Two types of turboshaft engines used to power a helicopter are:

    a. _____

    b. _____

45. Helicopters powered by reciprocating or direct-shaft turbine engines must use some form of

    _____ to disconnect the engine from the transmission during starting.

46. Helicopters must have some sort of _____ device to release the engine from the rotor any time

    the speed of the engine drops below that required to drive the rotor.

CHAPTER 2

SHEET METAL STRUCTURES

SECTION A
METALLIC AIRCRAFT CONSTRUCTION

1. The type of metal most often used in the construction of civilian aircraft is heat-treated

   _____ alloy.

2. The two basic types of sheet metal structure used for aircraft are:

   a. _____

   b. _____

3. A repair to an aircraft structure must restore its original:

   a. _____

   b. _____

   c. _____

4. The five basic stresses encountered by an aircraft structure are:

   a. _____

   b. _____

   c. _____

   d. _____

   e. _____

5. The top of a wing spar, in flight, is subjected to a _____ (tensile or compressive) stress.

6. The bottom of a wing spar, in flight, is subjected to a _____ (tensile or compressive) stress.

7. A torsional stress is made up of _____ and _____ acting

   perpendicular to each other.

8. A properly designed rivet joint is subjected to what types of stresses or loads?

   a. _____

   b. _____

9. If a properly designed rivet joint fails, the rivet first will _____ (pull out of the metal or shear).

10. Aircraft structures are most likely to fail at points where stresses _____ (concentrate or release) due to abrupt changes in _____ (direction or cross-sectional area)

11. To prevent a small crack from extending, you may _____ its end.

12. Aluminum alloys _____ (are or are not) susceptible to corrosion.

13. Name the primary alloying element in each of these aluminum alloys:

    a. 2117 _____

    b. 2024 _____

    c. 5056 _____

    d. 7075 _____

14. Commercially pure aluminum is identified by the number _____.

15. Most of the aluminum alloy used for aircraft structure is alloy number _____.

16. Alclad is _____ (pure aluminum, an anti-corrosion primer) that is _____ (sprayed, rolled) onto the surface of heat-treated aluminum alloys.

17. In order to protect the alloy within an Alclad sheet and to prevent creation of potential stress points, the surface of aircraft sheet metal should be protected from _____ and _____.

18. When an aluminum alloy is heated to its critical temperature and quenched, it is _____ (solution or precipitation) heat treated.

19. Artificial aging is another name for _____ (solution or precipitation) heat-treatment.

20. Aluminum alloys may be _____ (hardened or softened) by annealing.

21. Give the temper designation for each of these conditions:

    a. As fabricated _____

    b. Annealed _____

    c. Solution heat treated _____

    d. Solution heat treated and cold worked _____

    e. Solution heat treated and artificially aged _____

    f. Strain hardened to quarter-hard temper _____

    g. Strain hardened to full-hard temper _____

22. Magnesium is _____ (lighter or heavier) than aluminum.

23. Three drawbacks to the use of magnesium as a structural material are:

    a. _____

    b. _____

    c. _____

24. Titanium is used in structural areas of jet transports where a high _____ to _____ ratio is required

25. Because of it's strength and resistance to corrosion, stainless steel is well suited for _____(high or low) temperature applications such as:

    a. _____

    b. _____

26. Aluminum alloy-faced honeycomb panels are useful as a structural material because of their:

    a. _____

    b. _____

    c. _____

27. Three methods of corrosion prevention used on aluminum alloys are:

    a. _____

    b. _____

    c. _____

28. Three requirements for the formation of corrosion on aluminum alloy are:

    a. _____

    b. _____

    c. _____

29. Pure aluminum _____(will or will not) corrode.

30. A protective oxide film may be formed on the surface of a piece of aluminum alloy by what two methods?

    a. _____

    b. _____

SECTION B
SHEET METAL TOOLS AND FABRICATION

1. When using a scale for sheet metal layout, you _____(should or should not) measure from its end.

2. Scribes _____ (should or should not) be used to mark bend lines because

   _____.

3. If a lead pencil is used to make marks on turbine engine hot section parts or reciprocating engine exhaust systems, what can happen?

   _____

4. Felt marking pens _____(are or are not) widely used for sheet metal layout.

5. A _____ punch is used to locate the center of a rivet hole when using the old skin as a pattern for a new one.

6. A _____ punch is commonly used to remove rivets.

7. A _____ is a power or hand tool that is very useful for making detailed inside cuts.

8. Identify the color code for the handles of the aviation snips which:

   a. Cut right _____

   b. Cut left _____

   c. Cut straight _____

9. When using a deburring tool, avoid using too much pressure to prevent the hole from becoming

   _____.

10. The most commonly used shop tool for cutting sheet metal work is the _____ _____.

11. The three main parts of a twist drill are:

    a. _____

    b. _____

    c. _____

12. A number _____ drill is used to cut holes for 1/8" diameter rivets.

13. The _____ brake is the most widely used bending machine in aircraft maintenance shops.

14. What color is used to identify each of these Cleco fasteners?

    a. 3/32-inch _____

    b. 1/8-inch _____

    c. 5/32-inch _____

    d. 3/16-inch _____

15. A(n) _____ _____ is used for finding the location of new rivet

    holes when joining undrilled sheet metal skins over previously drilled skins.

16. A(n) _____ _____ is used to remove unwanted metal chips produced by drilling from

    between metal sheets.

17. Rivet length is measured in increments of _____-inch and rivet diameters are measured in increments of

    _____-inch.

18. Identify the head shape of each of these solid aluminum alloy rivets:

    a. AN426 (MS20426) _____

    b. AN470 (MS20470) _____

    c. AN430 _____

    d. AN442 _____

19. Prior to installing an AN426 rivet, the metal must be _____ or _____.

20. Identify the alloy used in solid aluminum rivets having these head identification characteristics:

    a. no mark _____

    b. dimple _____

    c. teat or raised dot _____

    d. raised dashes _____

    e. raised cross _____

21. Give the alloy number used for rivets identified by the following code letters:

    a. A_____

    b. B_____

    c. AD _____

    d. D _____

    e. DD _____

    f. E _____

22. Magnesium skins should be riveted using a rivet identified by the code letter _____.

23. 2017 Aluminum alloy rivets, identified by the code letter D must be _____ _____ before they
    can be driven. To maintain them in an annealed condition, they are quenched and immediately stored in a freezer.
    For this reason, they are commonly called _____ rivets.

24. Rivets that can be installed without access to both ends are called _____ rivets.

25. A(n) _____ is a special type of rivet that leaves a threaded hole for a machine screw after
    installation.

26. Three commonly used turn-lock fasteners used on cowlings, access panels, etc., are referred to by their trade names,
    and are called _____, _____ and _____
    fasteners.

SECTION C
SHEET METAL FABRICATION

1. On a properly driven rivet, the width of the bucked head must be _____ times the original shank diameter
    and the height must be _____ times the original shank diameter.

2. For a rivet joint to develop its required strength, no rivet should be installed with its center nearer to the edge of a
    sheet than _____ rivet diameters.

3. Adjacent rivets in a row should be no closer than _____ diameters, and no further apart
    than _____ to _____ diameters of the rivet shank.

4. The distance between rows of staggered rivets should be _____(what fraction) of the
    distance between rivets in a given row.

5. What size twist drill should be used for the installation of each of these rivet sizes?

        a. 3/32-inch _____

        b. 1/8-inch _____

        c. 5/32-inch _____

        d. 3/16-inch _____

6. The head angle of an MS20426 rivet is _____ degrees.

7. When three sheets of metal are dimpled and stacked to be riveted together, they should be
    _____(coin or radius) dimpled.

8. What type of dimpling is used on magnesium sheets to prevent them from cracking in the dimpling process?

   _____ dimpling.

9. An AN470DD6 rivet would be most properly driven with a(n) _____ (fast hitting or one-

   shot) rivet gun.

10. When installing rivets according to the N.A.C.A. method, the manufactured head is placed on the

    _____ (inside or outside) of the structure.

11. The tapping code used in team riveting is:

    a. Bad rivet _____ tap(s).

    b. Good rivet _____ tap(s).

    c. Drive the rivet some more _____ tap(s).

12. When practical, bends should be made _____ (across or with) the grain of the metal.

13. Indicate the minimum bend radius for each of these types of metal by referring to the bend radius chart in figure 2-

    127 of the *Jeppesen A&P Technician Airframe Textbook*.

    a. 0.032-inch 5052-O _____ inch.

    b. 0.032-inch 2024-T3 _____ inch.

    c. 0.064-inch 7075-T6 _____ inch.

14. The point of intersection of the mold lines of two sides of a bend is called the _____ point.

15. The distance from the mold point to the bend tangent line is known as the _____.

16. For a bend of 90 degrees, the setback is calculated using the formula:

    Setback = _____ + _____.

17. For a bend of more or less than 90°, we must apply a correction factor known as a(n)

    _____ -factor to find the setback.

18. The formula used to determine setback of an angle other than 90° is:

    Setback = _____

19. Find the setback for each of these bends:

    a. T = 0.040-inch   B.R.= 0.250-inch   Degrees = 90 Setback = _____

    b. T = 0.040-inch   B.R. = 0.250-inch   Degrees = 45 Setback = _____

    c. T = 0.040-inch   B.R. = 0.250-inch   Degrees = 135 Setback = _____

    d. T = 0.125 inch   B.R. = 0.50-inch   Degrees = 90 Setback = _____

20. The amount of material actually involved in the bend is known as the

    _____.

21. Using the bend allowance chart (figure 2-132) on page 2-74 of the text, find the bend allowance for each of these

    bends.

    a. T = 0.040-inch   B.R. = 0.250-inch   Degrees = 90

        B.A. = _____

    b. T = 0.032-inch   B.R. = 0.125-inch   Degrees = 90

        B.A. = _____

    c. T = 0.032-inch   B.R. = 0.125-inch   Degrees = 135

        B.A. = _____

    d. T = 0.051-inch   B.R. = 0.250-inch   Degrees = 45

        B.A. = _____

    e. T = 0.051-inch   B.R. = 0.250-inch   Degrees = 135

        B.A. = _____

22. When bending a bulb angle into a convex curve, the flange of the metal with the bulb must be

    _____(shrunk or stretched).

23. If a piece of metal becomes too hard when it is being bumped into a compound curve, it

    _____(may or may not) be annealed to soften it.

24. What is done to lightening holes in a wing rib to add stiffness? They may be _____.

25. In order for sheet metal pieces to be flat against the skin and yet have one flat on top of another, a process called

    _____ is used.

SECTION D
INSPECTION AND REPAIR OF METALLIC AIRCRAFT STRUCTURES

1. Shallow scratches in aluminum may be repaired by _____.

2. When repairing a damaged component or part, the technician should consult the manufacturer's

    _____ _____ manual.

3. The easiest way for a technician to assure that the FAA will approve a repair is to use _____ that has

    been _____ _____.

4. Approvals for return to service following a repair using approved data may be made by an A & P technician who

    holds an _____ _____.

5. What form must be completed when returning an aircraft to service following major structural repairs?

    FAA Form _____.

6. Why is an octagonal patch preferred over a rectangular patch in a high stressed aircraft structure?

    _____.

7. What diameter mechanical-lock Cherry rivet is normally used to replace an MS20470AD4 rivet?

    _____-inch diameter.

8. What may be used to replace a Hi-Shear rivet if you do not have the facilities to install another Hi-Shear rivet?

    _____

9. If the rivet spacing in the seams of a wing panel is not the same, which spacing should be copied when replacing a

    section of the panel?

    The same spacing as the nearest seam _____(inboard or outboard).

10. What tool is used to form a skin patch to the contour of the aircraft fuselage skin?

    _____.

11. When repairing aircraft floats, the rivets should be dipped in sealant and driven while they are

    _____(wet or dry).

12. Repairs to corrugated control surface skins are best performed by

    _____

13. A control surface repair must not _____(add or remove) weight behind the hinge line.

14. Prior to cutting an inspection hole to access an area needing repair, be sure that the _____ is in an

    _____ area.

15. A sheet metal repair to a pressurized structure may require the use of _____.

WOOD, COMPOSITE, AND TRANSPARENT PLASTIC STRUCTURES

CHAPTER 3

SECTION A
AIRCRAFT WOOD STRUCTURES

1. The reference wood for aircraft structures is _____ _____.

2. Evaluations of the quality of wood must take into account the:

   a. _____

   b. _____

   c. _____

3. Aviation-quality wood is usually _____ sawn to minimize _____.

4. The maximum slope of the grain for aviation-grade lumber is _____ to _____.

5. Two commonly used types of glue for modern wood aircraft construction are:

   a. _____

   b. _____

6. Sandpaper _____ (should or should not) be used to prepare a surface for gluing.

7. Almost all adhesives have four time periods that are critical to their use, they are:

   a. _____

   b. _____

   c. _____

   d. _____

8. _____ plywood, covered with aircraft fabric may be used as the external skin on some aircraft.

9. The _____ (lowest or highest) points inside an aircraft structure are the most likely places for wood deterioration to begin.

10. To prevent wood structure rotting, it should be treated with a(n) _____ sealer.

11. The best finish for internal wood structure is a good coat of high-quality _____.

12. If wood comes up in small chunks rather than splinters when it is picked with the point of a knife blade, it may be

    considered to be _____(good or rotted).

13. A wing spar _____(may or may not) be spliced under the fitting for a lift strut.

14. A splayed patch cannot be used in plywood skin that is more than _____ -inch thick.

15. The taper for a splayed patch is _____:1.

SECTION B
COMPOSITE STRUCTURES

1. Three advantages offered by composites are:

    a. _____

    b. _____

    c. _____

2. The three main parts of a fiber-reinforced composite are the:

    a. _____

    b. _____

    c. _____

3. The two common types of fiberglass are:

    a. _____

    b. _____

4. _____ is the name given to aromatic polymide fibers, such as Kevlar.

5. Because of its many excellent properties, Aramid is ideal for aircraft parts that are subject to _____

    _____ and _____.

6. Carbon fiber has high _____(compressive or tensile) strength, but promotes

    _____ (electrolytic or galvanic) corrosion when bonded to aluminum or steel.

7. Firewalls may be made of _____ fiber composites to dissipate the heat.

8. The strength of a fiber is _____(parallel or perpendicular) to the direction that the threads

    run.

9. The threads which run the length of the fabric as it comes off the bolt are referred to as the

    _____(warp or weft).

10. The tightly woven edge produced by the weavers to prevent the edges from raveling is referred to as the

    _____ edge.

11. The _____ is at a 45° angle to the warp threads.

12. Material in which all of the major fibers run in one direction, giving strength in that direction, are known as

    _____.

13. Chopped fibers that are compressed together are often called _____.

14. Fabrics are _____ (more or less) resistant to fiber breakout, delamination, and more

    damage tolerant than unidirectional materials.

15. The two categories of resin matrix systems are:

    a. _____

    b. _____

16. Thermoplastic and thermosetting resins have _____ (great or little) strength in themselves, and

    _____ (must be or need not be) reinforced with paper, cloth, or other filaments.

17. A thermoplastic resin _____ (will or will not) change shape if sufficiently re-heated while a

    thermosetting resin _____ (will or will not) change shape if re-heated.

18. Epoxy resin matrices are two-part systems consisting of a _____ and a _____. The _____

    acts as a curing agent by initiating a chemical reaction to harden the epoxy.

19. Pre-impregnated fabrics, or pre-pregs, are simply fabrics that have the _____ system

    already impregnated into the fabric.

20. Pre-preg fabrics must be kept _____ to prevent the resin from curing.

21. When the _____ (pot or shelf) life of a pre-preg fabric has expired it _____ (may or may not) be used

    for aircraft applications.

22. _____ are a popular thixotropic agent for use with thermosetting resins to give the resin

    good body with a minimum of weight.

23. In addition to microballoons, _____ _____ and _____ may be used

    as filler material when repairing composite structures.

24. Sandwich-construction core material may be made of:

    a. _____

    b. _____

    c. _____

25. The ribbon direction of a honeycomb core is the direction in which the honeycomb _____ (cannot or

    can) be pulled apart.

26. Closed cell styrofoam should be used with _____(epoxy or polyester) resin only.

27. _____ foam can be used with either epoxy or polyester resin.

28. The procedures for mixing resin systems _____(are or are not) very important.

29. _____ (Shelf life or Pot life) is the working life of a resin batch while _____ (shelf

    life or pot life) is the storage life of unopened resin containers.

30. What publications should be consulted to obtain information on the hazardous ingredients, health precautions,

    flammability characteristics, etc. of the various materials used in composite construction? _____

    _____ _____ _____.

31. What items of personal protective equipment are essential when working with composite chemicals?

    a. _____

    b. _____

    c. _____

32. When working with solvents and resins, it is important to take precautions against _____ and to always

    work in _____ _____ areas.

33. Two common solvents used in composite work are:

    a. _____

    b. _____

34. Five manufacturing methods that may be used with laminated construction are:

    a. _____

    b. _____

    c. _____

    d. _____

    e. _____

35. The purpose of the final finish on a composite structure is to:

    a. _____

    b. _____

36. What four methods are used to dissipate the electrical charge on composite structures?

    a. _____

    b. _____

    c. _____

    d. _____

37. Three common methods for inspecting and testing composite structures are:

    a. _____

    b. _____

    c. _____

38. The _____ _____ is a simple method of detecting delaminations close to the surface of a part.

39. To detect internal flaws or areas of delamination a(n) _____ _____ may be used.

40. Radiography (X-ray) _____(may or may not) be used to detect water inside honeycomb core cells.

41. _____ locates flaws by temperature variations at the surface of a damaged part.

42. Scissors with special steel blades with serrated edges are used to cut through _____ fabric.

43. Whenever possible composite materials should be _____ with wood when drilling.

44. You _____(should or should not) use a cutting coolant when drilling into bonded honeycomb or foam core structure.

45. _____(Steel, Carbide or Diamond) drills work on all types of composites and have long life.

46. While sanding, drilling, or trimming composite materials _____ must be worn to prevent breathing toxic fumes or dust.

47. Special brad point drills are available for drilling _____ (what type) composites.

48. Aluminum oxide sandpaper _____(should or should not) be used to sand carbon/graphite materials.

49. The older type fiberglass repairs _____(can or cannot) be used on advanced composite structures.

50. Repairs made to advanced composites using materials and techniques that have traditionally been used for fiberglass repairs will result in an _____ (airworthy or unairworthy) repair.

51. Damage to aircraft composite structure can usually be placed in one of these three categories:

     a. _____

     b. _____

     c. _____

52. Air-driven _____ are the best tools to use to remove damaged honeycomb core material from an aircraft structure.

53. _____ is the method that is usually used to remove advanced composite plies with the most control.

54. _____ cutting is used to remove damaged material with a tapered cutout.

55. The water break test is used to detect _____ or _____ contamination.

56. A(n) _____ _____ is a tool which can be used to reference the orientation of the warp of the fiber.

57. Mechanical pressure is used during the curing operation to:

     a. _____

     b. _____

     c. _____

     d. _____

     e. _____

58. _____ _____ is probably the most effective method to apply pressure to a repair.

59. Composite matrix systems may be divided according to type of curing and will be one of these two types:

     a. _____

     b. _____

60. The use of heat lamps to cure composite parts _____(is or is not) recommended.

61. Flexible silicon _____ _____ are the preferred method of applying heat to cure a composite component for repair work.

62. _____ curing is the process of raising the temperature to a point, holding it there, then raising the temperature, holding it at the new value, and continuing this process until the cure temperature is reached. After the cure time has elapsed, the reverse procedure will be used to slowly cool the material.

63. _____ films and _____ fabrics are used between a composite repair and other bagging materials to allow excess matrix materials to flow through to the upper surface.

64. _____ are absorbent materials which are used to soak up the excess resins.

65. Aluminum fasteners _____(should or should not) be used with carbon/graphite material.

66. If a puncture in the face of a honeycomb structure is minor (less than 1-inch), the repair may be made by

_____.

67. A _____ repair involves injection of resin and microballoons into a damaged area.

68. Separation of laminate layers or separation of the plies from the core material is called

_____.

69. A potted repair of minor damage to a structural component is considered to be _____ (permanent or temporary) while repairs to non-structural parts are _____ considered to be (permanent or temporary).

70. If a damaged area in a honeycomb core is too large to be repaired by a potted repair, it may be cleaned out and filled with a plug made of _____ material or _____ _____.

SECTION C
TRANSPARENT PLASTIC MATERIALS

1. Plastics, generally, may be classified as one of these two types:

    a. _____

    b. _____

2. In the U.S., the most frequently used transparent plastics for aircraft windows and windshields are:

    a. _____

    b. _____

3. Acetone _____(will or will not) soften acrylic plastic.

4. The most satisfactory way to store acrylic sheets is (circle a, b, or c)

    a. Store them horizontally.

    b. Store them vertically.

    c. Store them slightly away from the vertical.

5. When a plastic material has thousands of tiny cracks in its surface, it is said to be _____.

6. Soaking a sheet of acrylic plastic in boiling water is a(n) _____ (satisfactory or

    unsatisfactory) way of heating it into a formed shape.

7. The four methods for compound curve-forming for complex parts are:

    a. _____

    b. _____

    c. _____

    d. _____

8. When sawing acrylic sheets, it is important to feed the material _____ to avoid

    _____

9. The included angle for a twist drill used to drill acrylic plastic should be about _____

    degrees.

10. _____ _____ is a good material for softening acrylic plastic to

    glue it.

11. A cemented joint in acrylic plastic _____(does or does not) shrink as it becomes hard.

12. Curing acrylic plastics at an elevated temperature is also referred to as _____ _____.

13. Temporary repairs to acrylic windshields may be made with _____ _____ _____ or with small

    _____ and _____.

14. Acrylic windshields may be cleaned with _____ _____ and water.

15. When installing a new windshield, screw holes and the edges should have about _____ inch clearance to allow for

    _____.

AIRCRAFT WELDING

SECTION A
WELDING PROCESSES

1. _____ welding joins metals by blending compatible molten metals into one common part or joint.

2. _____ or nonfusion joining occurs when two or more pieces of steel are held together by a noncompatible molten brass or silver material.

3. The three basic types of fusion welding are:

    a. _____

    b. _____

    c. _____

4. Gas welding utilizes what two gases?

    a. _____

    b. _____

5. The temperature of a neutral oxyacetylene flame is about _____ degrees Fahrenheit.

6. Electric arc welding produces a blinding light with _____ and _____ rays which can _____ both skin and eyes.

7. Anyone performing electric arc welding must wear:

    a. An _____ _____ _____.

    b. _____

    c. _____

8. Shielded Metal Arc Welding (SMAW) is more commonly known as _____ welding.

9. MIG welding may also be known as _____ Arc Welding.

10. An uncoated wire is fed into the torch as a consumable electrode in _____ (TIG or MIG) welding.

11. The form of arc welding that fills most of the needs in aircraft maintenance is known as

    _____ _____ Arc Welding. This is commonly referred to by what

    three-letter designation? _____

12. A small wire of _____ is used as the non-consumable electrode for TIG welding.

13. In a TIG welder, the electric arc produces a temperature of up to _____ degrees

    Fahrenheit.

14. When using direct current for TIG welding, the most heat is put into the work when the DC is connected with

    _____(straight or reverse) polarity.

15. Two forms of electrical resistance welding are:

    a. _____

    b. _____

16. What three variables are controlled to get the proper weld using either of the two electrical resistance welding

    methods?

    a. _____

    b. _____

    c. _____

17. The five basic types of weld joints are the:

    a. _____ joint.

    b. _____ joint.

    c. _____ joint.

    d. _____ joint.

    e. _____ joint.

18. A cleanly formed oxyacetylene weld should encompass the following qualities:

    a. _____

    b. _____

    c. _____

    d. _____

19. Penetration of welded aircraft parts should be at a depth of _____ percent of the thickness

    of the base metal.

20. In brazing, the filler metal is pulled between closely fitting parts by _____ action.

21. When brazing, the filler rod should be melted by _____ (circle a or b).

    a. Holding the rod in the flame of the torch.

    b. Touching the rod to the hot metal.

22. Soft solder is a mixture of _____ and _____.

23. Fittings may be attached to stainless steel oxygen lines by _____ soldering.

SECTION B
ADVANCED WELDING AND REPAIRS

1. Aluminum _____ (does or does not) change its color as it melts.

2. Which gas is better for torch welding aluminum, acetylene or hydrogen? _____

3. The main advantage to oxyhydrogen welding is that the hydrogen flame burns much

    _____ (cleaner or hotter) than acetylene.

4. The flame used for welding aluminum should be neutral or slightly _____ (carburizing or

    oxidizing).

5. An _____ _____ shields the puddle of molten metal to prevent

    the formation of oxides when TIG welding.

6. Titanium must be welded in an atmosphere that prevents any _____ or _____ from

    contacting the hot metal.

7. Exhaust stacks from an aircraft engine should be TIG welded using _____ (DC or AC).

8. A dented structural tube may be repaired with a welded patch provided the dent is no deeper than _____ the

    tube diameter and doesn't involve more than _____ of the tube circumference.

9. A rosette weld is a form of _____ (lap or butt) weld.

10. The ends of a reinforcing tube used over a damaged tube in an aircraft structure can be cut with either a 30-degree

    _____ or a(n) _____.

11. Use of _____ _____ parts on a landing gear assembly makes welding repairs _____ or

    _____.

SECTION C
BASIC GAS WELDING

1. Acetylene gas stored under a pressure of more than _____ pounds per square inch will become unstable.

2. Normal operating pressure for most welding jobs using acetylene is _____ to _____ psi.

3. Acetylene gas may be stored under pressure by combining it with _____.

4. The amount of acetylene gas in a steel cylinder is determined by the _____(weight or pressure) of the cylinder.

5. The acetylene tank valve should be opened no more than _____ to _____ turn.

6. Oxygen must never be used in the presence of _____ based substances.

7. Tanks previously filled with _____, _____ or _____ fluid must be _____-_____ before beginning any welding operations.

8. Turning the acetylene regulator adjusting handle clockwise will _____(open or close) the valve.

9. The union nut for connecting the oxygen regulator to the cylinder valve has _____(right or left) hand threads.

10. The acetylene hose is colored _____ and has a _____(left or right) hand threaded fitting at each end.

11. The fittings on the _____(oxygen or acetylene) hose are identified by a groove cut around their hex nut fittings.

12. The oxygen hose is colored _____ and has a _____(left or right) hand threaded fitting at each end.

13. The torch most often used with cylinder gases is an _____(equal-pressure or injector)-type.

14. A torch designed for light-duty welding, such as one used with aircraft thin wall tubing, has its valve on the end of the torch near the _____ (tip or hoses).

15. The lower the number of the welding tip (not the size of the orifice), the _____(smaller or larger) the tip.

16. The size of the orifice in a welding tip is measured with the shank of a(n) _____

    _____.

17. Torches should be lit with a(n) _____, not with _____.

18. Most mild steel filler rods are coated with _____ to prevent rust from forming on the

    surface of the rod.

19. Oxyacetylene welding goggles _____ (will or will not) provide adequate eye protection for

    electric arc welding.

20. The lower the number of the welding goggle filter, the _____ (lighter or darker) the filter.

21. A _____ (blue or brown) filter should be used in the welding goggles for welding

    aluminum.

22. The _____ of the metal to be welded will determine the size of the torch tip needed.

23. An oxyacetylene flame in which the feather of the outer cone just disappears into the inner cone is a(n)

    _____ (oxidizing, neutral, or carburizing) flame.

24. The pre-heat flame in an oxyacetlyene cutting torch should be adjusted to a(n)

    _____ (neutral or oxidizing) flame.

25. When an oxyacetylene welding torch is shut off, the _____ (oxygen or acetylene) is shut off first.

CHAPTER 5

AIRCRAFT FABRIC COVERING

SECTION A
FABRIC COVERING PROCESSES

1. The clear dope film and organic fabric such as cotton and linen are protected from damage by the sun by mixing extremely fine flakes of _____ in with the dope.

2. Which is more flammable, cellulose nitrate or cellulose butyrate dope?

    _____.

3. Recovering an aircraft in the same manner as was used by the manufacturer _____ (is or is not) considered to be a major repair.

4. Three sources of approved data for recovering an airplane are:

    a. _____

    b. _____

    c. _____

5. The minimum tensile strength of new grade-A cotton fabric is _____ pounds per square inch.

6. The fabric on an aircraft with a wing loading of 9.5 pounds per square foot and a never-exceed speed of 180 miles per hour can deteriorate to _____ pounds per square inch before it is considered to be unairworthy.

7. _____ fabric may be used to cover a plywood structure to give it an extremely smooth finish.

8. The two most common synthetic fabrics are made of:

    a. _____

    b. _____

9. _____ tape is used for inter-rib bracing to hold the wing ribs in their upright position until the fabric is stitched to them.

10. _____ tape is used to cover all the seams, over all the ribs, around the tips, and along the

trailing edge of all the surfaces.

11. Drainage grommets are usually applied with the _____(what number) coat of dope.

12. Drainage grommets should be opened by _____(cutting or punching) the center out.

13. _____ _____ are installed where access to the interior structure may be

required.

14. _____ is a special slow-drying solvent that prevents rapid evaporation of aircraft dope.

15. The dope in which the fungicidal paste is mixed should be applied to the fabric

_____(thinned or full strength).

16. One pound of aluminum powder should be mixed with _____ gallons of unthinned clear

dope, for the aluminum dope coats.

17. Rejuvenator _____(will or will not) restore strength to deteriorated fabric.

18. Rejuvenator is a mixture of potent solvents and _____.

SECTION B
COVERING PROCEDURES

1. Fabric is considered to be airworthy until it has less than _____% of its original strength.

2. The principle advantage of a Maule tester over a Seybolt tester is that it does not _____ the fabric if

the fabric is still good.

3. The parts of an aircraft most susceptible to deterioration are locations that are:

    a. _____

    b. _____

4. All of the interior wood members of an aircraft should be given a coat of _____ before

the structure is recovered.

5. A(n) _____ stitch is used for hand sewing the fabric along the trailing edge of the wing.

6. A _____ _____ knot is used to secure rib stitches.

7. Two methods of applying the fabric to an aircraft structure are:

    a. the _____ method.

    b. the _____ method.

8. Wrinkles are removed from cotton fabric after it is installed on an aircraft structure by spraying it with

    _____.

9. The first coat of dope applied to cotton fabric should contain a _____ additive.

10. The recommended brush for applying aircraft dope should have _____ (animal or

    synthetic) bristles.

11. The first coat of dope applied to cotton fabric will cause the fabric to _____(tighten or

    loosen).

12. Anti-tear strips should be used under the reinforcing tape on aircraft having a never-exceed speed in excess of

    _____ miles per hour.

13. A wing rib of an airplane with a never-exceed speed of 200 miles per hour should have a stitch spacing every

    _____ inches in the slipstream and every _____ inches outside

    of the slipstream.

14. Rib stitch knots should be placed _____(in the center or beside) the reinforcing tape on a

    wing rib.

15. A(n) _____ knot is used to join two pieces of waxed rib stitch cord.

16. Before a fabric-covered aircraft structure is dry-sanded, it should be electrically _____.

17. The surface tape along the trailing edge of a control surface should be notched every 18 inches if the airplane has a

    never exceed speed of _____ miles per hour or more.

18. The glass-like surface of a doped finish comes from the _____(clear or aluminum) dope

    coats.

19. Separation of the finish can be caused by too _____(much or little) aluminum powder in

    the dope used for the aluminum dope coats.

20. Properly applied aluminum dope coats will dry with a slightly _____ (glossy or dull)

    finish.

21. _____(Butyrate or Nitrate) dope should be used on treated glass cloth that is used to cover

    an airframe.

SECTION C
INSPECTION AND REPAIR OF FABRIC COVERING

1. The first coat of dope applied to a glass cloth covering should be _____(brushed or

    sprayed) on.

2. When making a sewed repair to an L-shaped tear in an aircraft covering, you should use a(n)

    _____ stitch and should start sewing at the _____(apex or end)

    of the tear.

3. When using a baseball stitch to repair an L-shaped tear, you should use a minimum of

    _____ stitches per inch, and lock the stitches every _____ to

    _____ stitches with a modified seine knot.

4. When repairing the fabric of an aircraft that has a never-exceed speed greater than 150 miles per hour, you should

    _____ (sew or dope) the patch in place.

CHAPTER 6

AIRCRAFT PAINTING AND FINISHING

SECTION A
FABRIC FINISHING PROCESSES

1. _____ are used in aircraft dope to make its film flexible.

2. A dope film should be scrubbed with _____ _____ and water and any wax removed with an appropriate solvent before the rejuvenator is sprayed on.

3. Rejuvenator is a mixture of potent _____ and _____.

4. Rejuvenators restore the _____ to a dried-out dope film.

5. Finish coats of dope should be sprayed on with a _____(heavy or light) coat.

6. Colored dope may be given a glossier finish by mixing it with up to _____% clear dope.

7. The topcoats of a doped finish may peel off if there is _____ (too much or too little) aluminum powder in the aluminum dope coats.

8. A dope film blushes when _____ condenses out of the air into the freshly applied dope film.

9. Mixing _____ with the dope will prevent blushing if the conditions are not too severe.

10. The relative humidity of the air may be lowered to prevent blushing by _____(warming or cooling) the air.

11. Two causes for pinholes in a dope film are:

    a. _____

    b. _____

12. Three causes for runs and sags in a dope surface are:

    a. _____

    b. _____

    c. _____

13. Orange peel in a dope surface may be caused by:

    a. _____

    b. _____

    c. _____

14. Localized spots within the dope film that do not dry are called _____.

15. Dope that is brushed on too heavy or brushed when it is too cold will cause dope _____.

16. Two disadvantages of a polyurethane finish on a fabric-covered surface are:

    a. _____

    b. _____

17. Spraying the newer polyurethane materials over a special _____ _____ _____ makes them suitable for use over fabric surfaces.

18. Polyurethane material should be removed from a damaged surface with _____ before a repair can be made.

SECTION B
AIRCRAFT PAINTING PROCESSES

1. The three basic techniques for stripping paint from metal surfaces are:

    a. _____

    b. _____

    c. _____

2. The potent, possibly toxic ingredients in chemical strippers must be used with care to prevent:

    a. _____

    b. _____

3. The use and disposal of chemical strippers is strictly regulated by the _____ and

    _____.

4. Parts of an aircraft surface that must not be touched with paint stripper may be masked with:

    a. _____

    b. _____

5. Paint stripper should be brushed on in a _____(thick or thin) layer.

6. Stripper residue is cleaned from an aircraft surface with _____ or

   _____.

7. Sand blasting _____(is or is not) a good method for removing paint from aircraft structure or parts.

8. New media blasting systems use _____ material to remove the old finish and surface

   corrosion.

9. Filiform corrosion may occur under the dense film of _____(polyurethane or acrylic)

   topcoats.

10. A(n) _____ coating changes the surface of an aluminum alloy into an oxide film that is

    chemically inert and will not allow filiform corrosion.

11. Two common primer materials are:

    a. _____

    b. _____

12. Most high-volume production all-metal aircraft are primed with a(n) _____ primer.

13. Wash primer is made up of these three components:

    a. _____

    b. _____

    c. _____

14. Wash primers should be applied with a maximum film thickness of _____ mil.

15. If the topcoat is not applied over the wash primer within _____ hours, another coat of primer must be

    applied over the first one.

16. About the most critical aspect of the application of wash primers is the necessity to have sufficient

    _____ in the air to properly convert the acid into a phosphate film.

17. Acrylic lacquer has a _____(high or low) solids content.

18. The best finish produced by an acrylic lacquer will result from (circle a or b)

    a. A few heavy coats of finish sprayed on.

    b. Several light coats of finish sprayed on.

19. The most durable finish system and the one that gives the most pleasing appearance is produced by the

    _____ system.

20. _____ primer may be used under a polyurethane topcoat, but if it is not properly cured, it may cause filiform corrosion.

21. After mixing polyurethane with its catalyst, it must be allowed to stand for 15 to 30 minutes. This is called the _____ time of the material.

22. The viscosity of a thinned finishing material is determined using a(n)

_____.

23. A polyurethane finish is usually dry enough to be taped after _____ hours of drying time, but it is best to wait _____ hours.

24. The time between the mixing of a catalyzed material and the time it has set up too much for it to be used is called the _____ life of the material.

25. High visibility finishes consist of three layers: a _____ _____ base coat, a coat of _____ _____ and an _____ - _____ topcoat.

26. An acid-proof finish, far superior to asphaltum or bituminous paint, is a good coat of _____ enamel.

27. Zinc chromate paste that is used for making leak-proof seams _____(will or will not) harden.

28. _____ oil is used to protect the inside of the tubular structure in aircraft fuselages, empennage structure, and landing gear.

SECTION C
FINISHING EQUIPMENT AND SAFETY

1. Most of the fumes from finishing materials are _____ (heavier or lighter) than air.

2. All filter units and water traps in the shop air system should be drained _____ (what interval).

3. Powder coating, or "dry painting" is usually reserved for parts such as _____ _____ and _____ _____ _____.

4. The two basic spray gun types use either _____ feed or _____ feed.

5. Filter-type masks when worn by spray painters _____(will or will not) filter out the paint

   fumes.

6. Paint mixing agitators should be driven by an _____ drill motor, never with an

   _____ drill motor.

7. A correctly adjusted spray gun should produce a uniform fan-shaped spray, with the fan

   _____(parallel or perpendicular) to the wing ports.

8. An excessive overspray may be caused by too _____(much or little) atomizing air

   pressure.

9. Match the spray pattern with the number that identifies the cause of the distortion.

1.   2.   3.   4.   5.

   a.   _____ Material too thick for the amount of atomizing air.

   b.   _____ Plugged-up wing port hole on one side.

   c.   _____ Normal spray pattern.

   d.   _____ Too much air through the wing port holes for the amount of material that is being sprayed.

   e.   _____ Material buildup in the air cap.

10. "When painting an airplane, you should paint the corners and edges first, then the flat surfaces." This statement is

    _____(true or false).

11. Each pass made by a paint spray gun should overlap the previous pass by about

    _____(what fraction) of their width.

12. When an airplane is sprayed, the painting should be done so the overspray falls

    _____(ahead of or behind) the area being painted.

13. Immediately after use, all spray equipment should be cleaned with _____.

14. An extremely thin _____ masking tape provides the sharpest lines for trim colors.

15. The location and size of registration numbers required on an aircraft are specified in Federal Aviation Regulations

    Part _____.

16. The Roman letter _____ preceding the registration numbers must be placed on all civil aircraft

    registered in the United States of America.

17. How much length would be required to lay out the numbers N469AB, if the numbers are 12 inches high?

    _____ inches.

18. A ball-point pen is a _____ (good or bad) tool to use to mark the surface of an aircraft when

    laying out the registration numbers.

19. Decals are applied by soaking them in clean warm _____ until the clear portion slides

    easily from the backing.

20. Dried overspray on the paint shop floor should be removed by — _____ (wet or dry)

    sweeping it.

AIRFRAME ELECTRICAL SYSTEMS

CHAPTER 7

SECTION A
AIRBORNE SOURCES OF ELECTRICAL POWER

1. In any generator, current will flow whenever there is _____ motion between the wire coil and the magnetic field.

2. The strength of the induced current depends on the _____ of the magnetic field and the _____ at which the lines of flux are cut.

3. What does each of the three digits represent in the left-hand rule for generators?

    a. First finger _____

    b. Middle finger _____

    c. Thumb _____

4. The coil of wire in a generator where the current is induced is called the _____.

5. The device that converts the AC current produced in the armature into DC current is called the

    _____.

6. Current is transferred from the rotating commutator to stationary _____.

7. The principle parts of a small aircraft DC generator are the:

    a. _____

    b. _____

    c. _____

    d. _____

8. The field frame of a generator has two primary functions. They are to:

    a. _____

    b. _____

9. The magnetizing force inside a generator is produced by an electromagnet called a _____ coil and a core called the _____ _____ or _____.

10. Each brush is connected to the external circuit by a flexible braided-copper _____.

11. Brushes are made of high-grade _____ to prevent undue wear on the _____ yet still have a reasonable service life.

12. Generators may be constructed in one of three ways. They may be:

    a. _____ wound.

    b. _____ wound.

    c. _____ wound.

13. _____ wound generators are not used in aircraft because of poor voltage regulation characteristics.

14. Compound-wound generators combine features of both series and shunt wound generators and may be one of three types: _____ compounded, _____ compounded or_____ compounded.

15. The distortion of the magnetic field between the generator poles caused by the magnetic field created by the armature current is called _____ _____.

16. The position where the plane of two opposite coils is perpendicular to the magnetic field of the generator is called the _____ plane.

17. Some generators use _____ to counter the effect of armature reaction.

18. The speed at which a generator begins to produce its rated voltage is called the _____-_____ speed and is usually about _____ RPM.

19. Varying the _____ current controls generator output.

20. The three relays contained in a three-unit voltage regulator are:

    a. _____.

    b. _____.

    c. _____.

21. DC generators employ a _____ _____ relay between the generator output terminal and the bus to prevent the battery from discharging through the generator.

22. Residual magnetism may be restored to a generator by _____ the field.

23. A variety of tests can be performed on DC generator and motor armatures with a specially designed test unit called a _____.

24. Large aircraft use AC alternators because they can produce a _____ amount of power and are _____ in weight.

25. The principle difference between a DC generator and a DC alternator is that the magnetic field is _____

    (stationary or moving) in a generator and _____ (stationary or moving) in an alternator.

26. The alternating current produced in a DC alternator is changed into direct current with a

    _____(solid-state or mechanical) rectifier.

27. The principle parts of an alternator are the:

    a. _____

    b. _____

    c. _____

    d. _____

28. Carbon brushes, riding on smooth _____ _____ carry the field current from the voltage regulator to the

    alternator rotor.

29. Solid-state voltage regulators are usually _____ (repaired or replaced) if they fail.

30. A reverse-current cutout relay _____(is or is not) necessary with a DC alternator.

31. A _____ phase alternator is used for almost all aircraft applications.

32. If one lead from each winding of a three-phase alternator is connected to a common point, the stator is

    _____ connected and if the phases are connected end-to-end the stator is _____ connected.

33. Modern jet aircraft typically use an _____ cooled _____(brush-type or brushless) alternator.

34. On jet aircraft a _____ _____ _____

    unit is used between the engine and the alternator to assure a constant frequency output.

35. Alternators used on large aircraft generally supply _____ (how many) hertz, _____ (how many)

    phase alternating current.

36. The most commonly used aircraft batteries are the _____-_____ battery and the _____-

    _____ battery.

37. The state of charge of a lead acid battery is determined by measuring the _____ _____ of

    the electrolyte.

38. The specific gravity of a fully charged lead-acid battery should be between _____ and _____ at 80 deg.

    Fahrenheit (27 deg. Celsius).

39. The specific gravity of a discharged lead-acid battery is about _____.

40. The specific gravity of a lead-acid battery is checked with a _____.

41. The open circuit voltage of a lead-acid cell is approximately _____ volts.

42. Battery capacity is measured in _____-_____.

43. The standard rating used to specify battery capacity is the _____-_____ rating.

44. Batteries must be kept _____ and the terminals must be kept _____ and free of

    _____.

45. Corrosion and deposits can be removed from a lead-acid battery or battery box by scrubbing with a soft

    _____ _____ and a solution of _____ _____ and water.

46. Care should be taken to avoid getting any baking soda in the cells of a lead-acid battery because baking soda

    _____ the electrolyte.

47. If it becomes necessary to dilute acid to make electrolyte, it is extremely important that you always add the

    _____ to the _____ and never the other way around.

48. The two methods for charging a battery are the constant-_____ method and the constant-_____

    method. Aircraft generating systems use the constant-_____ method.

49. The two functions of an aircraft generating system are to:

    a. _____

    b. _____

50. In order to charge a 24-volt battery, the alternator must produce about _____ volts, and for a 12-volt battery,

    about _____ volts.

51. Spilled electrolyte from a lead-acid battery should be neutralized with _____ _____ and

    rinsed with _____.

52. Nickel-cadmium batteries have a _____(low or high) internal resistance.

53. To minimize the possibility of "thermal runaway," aircraft that are equipped with nickel-cadmium batteries will

    have a battery _____ warning system installed.

54. The specific gravity of the electrolyte in a nickel-cadmium battery _____ (is or is not) a

    measure of the state of charge of the battery.

55. It is extremely important that nickel-cadmium and lead-acid batteries be serviced in separate areas because the

    electrolytes are _____ _____ and their fumes will _____ each other.

56. Spilled nickel-cadmium electrolyte can be neutralized with _____ _____ or _____.

57. The only way to determine the actual condition of a nickel-cadmium battery is to _____ _____ it, then

    discharge it at a specified rate to measure its _____-_____ capacity.

SECTION B
AIRCRAFT ELECTRICAL SYSTEMS

1. An electrical schematic diagram shows the _____ (relationship or physical location) of all the electrical components and associated wiring in a particular system.

2. A clipping diode may be installed across the coil of the master relay to eliminate _____ _____ that could damage sensitive electronic components.

3. The term _____ is often used to define a heavy current solenoid, such as the one used to energize the starter.

4. Identify these statements as True or False concerning the landing gear circuit shown in figure 7-63A in the *Jeppesen A&P Technician Airframe Text.*

    a. All three landing gear must be down and locked before any of the down-and-locked lights will illuminate. _____

    b. The landing gear selector switch cannot be placed in the GEAR UP position when the weight of the aircraft is on the landing gear. _____

    c. If the landing gear is not down and locked, the warning horn will sound any time the throttle is closed, regardless of the position of the landing gear switch. _____

    d. The pump motor cannot run in the GEAR UP direction when the weight of the aircraft is on the landing gear. _____

5. Vibrator type voltage regulators with provisions for paralleling two generators have an extra _____ that is connected to a paralleling switch or relay.

6. The only current that flows in the paralleling coils is that caused by the difference in the output _____ (voltage or current) of the two generators.

7. The two basic types of large aircraft electrical bus distribution systems are the:

    a. _____

    b. _____

8. On aircraft equipped with a _____ (split-bus or parallel-bus) system, all generators are connected to a common bus and share the load equally.

SECTION C
WIRING INSTALLATION

1. The insulation on aircraft wire is designed to withstand _____ volts.

2. _____-gauge wire is the smallest size aluminum wire recommended for use in aircraft electrical circuits.

3. The _____ _____ gauge is used to indicate the size of electrical wire.

4. Fill in the allowable voltage drop for each of these system conditions by referring to the chart in figure 7-81 in the *Jeppesen A&P Technician Airframe Textbook.*

    a. 15 Amp intermittent load with a 25 foot wire length in a 28-volt system: _____ volt/volts.

    b. 5 Amp continuous load with a 10 foot wire length in a 14-volt system: _____volt(s).

    c. 15 Amp intermittent load with a wire length of 60 feet in a 115-volt system: _____volt(s).

    d. 20 Amp continuous load with a 40 foot wire length in a 200-volt system: _____volt(s).

5. Using the electrical wire chart in figure 7-82 in the *Jeppesen A&P Technician Airframe Textbook,* determine what gauge wire would be best suited for each of these conditions:

    a. A continuous load in a 14-volt system needing 40 feet of wire to carry 30 amps. The wire is to be routed in a bundle. _____-gauge

    b. An intermittent load of 200 amps in a 28-volt system. The wire is 12 feet long and routed in free air. _____-gauge

    c. A continuous load of 20 amps in a 115-volt system. The wire is to be routed in a bundle and is 120 feet long. _____-gauge

    d. An intermittent load of 300 amps in a 14-volt system. The wire is 6 feet long and is routed in free air. _____-gauge

6. Wires must have an identification mark every _____ to _____ inches.

7. When electrical wires are routed parallel to lines carrying oxygen or any type of liquid, the wiring should be at least _____ inches _____(above or below) the fluid lines.

8. When electrical wiring is run through conduit, the conduit should be approximately

_____% larger than the diameter of the wire bundle.

9. Encasing a wire in a braided metal jacket is called _____ the wire.

10. What color insulated terminal would be used on each of these wire sizes:

   a. 20-guage _____

   b. 10-guage _____

   c. 14-guage _____

11. The strength of a properly crimped wire terminal will be _____ (less than, equal to, or

   more than) the strength of the wire.

12. No more than _____(how many) wire terminals may be connected to a single stud on a

   terminal strip.

13. Bonding jumpers should have a resistance of no more than _____ ohms.

14. A _____ cable consists of a central conductor surrounded by an insulator and a second

   conductor.

15. The _____ connector is probably the most widely used terminal on coaxial cable attached to aircraft radio

   antennas.

SECTION D
ELECTRICAL SYSTEM COMPONENTS

1. In what Federal Aviation Administration publication may a switch derating factor table be found?

   _____

2. Switches must be installed in a _____ and _____ manner. This means that moving a switch

   _____ or _____ turns power on to the circuit.

3. A SPST switch has _____(how many) contacts and controls _____ circuit(s).

4. Normally a _____(relay or solenoid) has a fixed iron core.

5. A _____(what type) fuse has a fusible element that is held under tension by a small coil

   spring.

6. All aircraft circuit breakers must be of the _____-_____ type.

7. The three basic configurations of circuit breakers used on aircraft are:

    a. _____

    b. _____

    c. _____

8. Indicate the color of lens used for each navigation light position listed:

    a. Left wing _____

    b. Right wing _____

    c. Tail _____

9. Anti-collision lights may be either of these two types:

    a. _____

    b. _____

10. Always allow a strobe system to sit in the OFF position for at least _____ minutes prior

    to any maintenance operation.

11. What does each of the three fingers represent in the right-hand rule for motors?

    a. First finger _____

    b. Second finger _____

    c. Thumb _____

12. The stationary magnetic field in a DC electric motor may be produced by:

    a. _____

    b. _____

13. Three types of field-armature circuit arrangements used in DC motors are:

    a. _____

    b. _____

    c. _____

14. Series-connected DC motors have a _____ (high or low) starting torque.

15. An aircraft starter uses a _____ (series or shunt)-wound DC motor.

16. The three types of AC motors are the:

    a. _____ motor.

    b. _____ motor.

    c. _____ motor.

17. The speed of an AC induction motor is determined by:

    a. _____

    b. _____

HYDRAULIC AND PNEUMATIC POWER SYSTEMS

CHAPTER 8

SECTION A
PRINCIPLES OF HYDRAULIC POWER

1. Hydraulic systems have many advantages, including:

    a. _____

    b. _____

    c. _____

    d. _____

2. Hydraulic systems are almost _____% efficient.

3. Hydraulic fluid is considered to be _____ (compressible or incompressible).

4. The pressure exerted by a column of liquid is determined by the _____.

    (height of the column or the volume of the container)

5. Pascal's Law, the basic law for transmitting hydraulic power states that pressure in a closed system is transmitted

    _____ and _____ to _____(all or some) parts of the system.

6. Force per unit area is a measure of _____.

7. The relationship between Force, Area, and Pressure may be expressed using the formula

    _____.

8. In a hydraulic system the relationship between the area of the piston, the distance it moves, and the volume of the

    fluid displaced may be expressed using the formula _____.

9. What are the two major advantages of a hydraulic system over mechanical systems?

    a. _____

    b. _____

10. Use the following figure to answer a through d below.

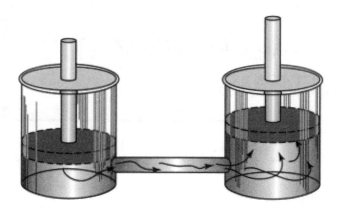

Cylinder 1
Piston diameter = 2 inches

Cylinder 2
Piston diameter = 3 inches

a. If the force pushing down on the actuator rod of cylinder 1 is 100 pounds, the force exerted by the actuating

rod of cylinder 2 will be _____ pounds.

b. If the piston in cylinder-1 moves 5 inches, the piston in cylinder-2 will move

_____inches.

c. A force of _____ pounds will have to be exerted on the piston in cylinder-1 to

produce a force of 1,000 pounds on the piston in cylinder-2.

d. If the pressure inside cylinder-1 is 500 psi, the pressure inside cylinder-2 will be

_____ psi.

11. Use the following figure to answer a (below) and b (on the following page).

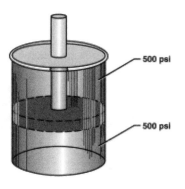

500 psi

500 psi

a. If a pressure of 500 psi is applied to both sides of the piston in this cylinder, the piston will move

_____(up, down, or will not move).

b. If the piston diameter is 4 inches and the actuator rod diameter is ¾ inches, the resultant force produced by

the actuating rod will be _____pounds.

SECTION B
HYDRAULIC SYSTEM COMPONENTS AND DESIGN

1. A good hydraulic fluid must possess these properties:

    a. _____.

    b. _____.

    c. _____.

    d. _____.

    e. _____.

2. _____ is the internal resistance to flow of a liquid.

3. The _____ _____ is the temperature at which a liquid will give off vapor in sufficient quantity

    to ignite momentarily.

4. The three types of hydraulic fluid currently being used in civilian aircraft are:

    a. _____.

    b. _____.

    c. _____.

5. It _____ (is or is not) permissible to mix different types of hydraulic fluid.

6. Vegetable base hydraulic fluid is essentially _____ oil and

    _____.

7. Vegetable base hydraulic fluid is dyed _____ for identification.

8. The most widely used hydraulic fluid in general aviation aircraft today is _____.

9. What type of hydraulic fluid is dyed red for identification? _____.

10. Synthetic hydraulic fluids were developed to provide a(n) _____-resistant hydraulic fluid

    for use in high performance piston and turbine aircraft.

11. Skydrol is _____ in color.

12. If Skydrol is accidently spilled, it should be immediately cleaned up using _____ and

    _____.

13. Name the fluid that may be used to flush hydraulic systems using each of the following types of hydraulic fluid:

    a. Vegetable-base _____

    a. Mineral-base _____

    b. Synthetic _____

14. Name the material used for seals in hydraulic systems using each of the following types of hydraulic fluids:

    b. Vegetable-base _____

    c. Mineral-base _____

    d. Synthetic _____

SECTION C
HYDRAULIC POWER SYSTEMS

1. Virtually all modern airplanes use a simple hydraulic system to operate the _____.

2. A hydraulic system must contain four basic types of units; these are:

    a. _____

    b. _____

    c. _____

    d. _____

3. A single unit containing an electrically driven hydraulic pump, reservoir, control valve and many of the auxiliary valves is known as a hydraulic _____ _____ system.

4. The two types of hydraulic reservoirs are:

    a. _____

    b. _____

5. Aircraft that operate in the lower altitudes normally use _____ (pressurized or unpressurized) hydraulic reservoirs.

6. Three ways of pressurizing a hydraulic reservoir are:

    a. _____

    b. _____

    c. _____

7. One micron is equal to _____ inch.

8. Pleated paper micronic filters are usually installed in the hydraulic system _____(pressure or return) line.

9. Cuno filters _____(can or cannot) be used on the pressure side of the hydraulic system.

10. _____ (Single or Double) - action pumps are the most common type of hand pump.

11. A _____(constant or variable) displacement pump moves a specific volume of fluid each time its shaft turns.

12. A(n) _____ valve of some sort is needed when a constant displacement pump is used.

13. A gear-type hydraulic pump is a _____ (constant or variable) displacement pump.

14. A hydraulic system using a variable displacement pump _____ (does or does not) require an unloading valve.

15. A selector valve is one of the most common types of _____ (flow or pressure)-control valves.

16. The _____(open or closed)-center valve directs fluid through the center of the valve back to the reservoir when a unit is not being actuated.

17. A valve that allows free flow of fluid in one direction, but no flow in the opposite direction is called a(n) _____ valve.

18. A valve that allows free flow of fluid in one direction but a restricted flow in the opposite direction is called a(n) _____ _____ valve.

19. A valve that requires one component to fully actuate before another can actuate is called a(n) _____ valve.

20. _____ valve are similar to sequence valves except they are opened by hydraulic pressure rather than by mechanical contact.

21. A(n) _____ _____ may be installed to block a line in case of a serious leak.

22. Two principles upon which a hydraulic fuse may operate are:

   a. _____

   b. _____

23. The simplest type of pressure control valve is the _____ valve.

24. A(n) _____ _____ may be installed when it is necessary to operate some portion of a hydraulic system at a pressure lower than the normal system pressure.

25. A(n) _____ is a simple device designed to store hydraulic fluid under pressure.

26. One compartment of an accumulator is connected to the hydraulic system, and the other compartment is filled with compressed _____ or _____.

27. Three types of accumulators used in aircraft hydraulic systems are:

    a. _____

    b. _____

    c. _____

28. High pressure valve cores are identified by the letter _____ embossed on the end of their stem.

29. Hydraulic actuators which produce straight-line movement are known as _____ actuators.

30. If a continuous rotational force is needed, a hydraulic _____ may be used.

31. A chevron seal is a _____(one-way or two-way) seal.

32. An O-ring is a _____(one-way or two-way) seal.

33. An O-ring should have a width of approximately 10% _____(larger or smaller) than the width of the groove into which it fits.

34. A _____ _____ should be used with an O-ring whenever the operating pressure exceeds about _____ psi.

35. The _____ date is the date of O-ring manufacture.

36. An O-ring marked with a blue dot _____(would or would not) be compatible with MIL-H-5606 hydraulic fluid.

37. When installing O-rings, extreme care must be used to prevent the ring from being _____ or _____ by sharp edges.

SECTION D
AIRCRAFT PNEUMATIC SYSTEMS

1. The air for _____(high, medium, or low) pressure pneumatic systems is usually stored in metal bottles.

2. Medium pressure pneumatic systems on turbine powered aircraft usually use _____ air for their operation.

3. One of the most common types of aircraft pneumatic systems supplies low-pressure air to operate _____

_____.

4. _____(vane or piston)-type pumps are usually associated with low pressure pneumatic

systems, such as those used to operate aircraft instruments.

5. After the air in a pneumatic system leaves the moisture separator it must pass through a(n)

_____ or _____ _____, to remove the

last traces of moisture.

6. A(n) _____ valve may be installed to allow a pneumatic system to operate from a ground

source.

7. Emergency extension air enters a hydraulic landing gear actuator through a(n) _____

valve.

AIRCRAFT LANDING GEAR SYSTEMS

SECTION A
LANDING GEAR SYSTEMS AND MAINTENANCE

1. The tailwheel type landing gear arrangement is also known as _____ landing gear.

2. Retracting the landing gear on an aircraft decreases the _____(induced or parasite) drag.

3. Almost all current production airplanes use the _____-type landing gear arrangement.

4. Tailwheel aircraft are highly susceptible to an abrupt, uncontrolled change in direction on the ground called a

    _____ _____ due to the relationship between the main wheels and the _____

    _____ _____.

5. The streamlined fairings used to enclose the wheels are referred to as _____

    _____.

6. A(n) _____ cord is a bundle of small strands of rubber encased in a loosely woven cloth

    tube.

7. The most widely used shock absorber for aircraft is the _____-

    _____ shock absorber or more commonly known as an _____

    strut.

8. An oleo strut absorbs the landing impact shock with the _____(air or oil).

9. An oleo strut absorbs the taxi shocks with the _____(air or oil).

10. Oleo strut inflation is checked by measuring the length of the exposed _____

    _____.

11. Modern aircraft wheels are almost always _____ (one or two)-piece units.

12. Aircraft wheels may be cast or forged of either _____ or _____

    alloy.

13. The _____ _____ area is the most critical part of a wheel.

14. Steel keys or keyways on the inboard wheel half drive the rotating _____ _____.

15. One or more _____ _____ may be installed in the inboard half of

the main wheels of jet aircraft to release the air from the tire in case of extreme overheating.

16. Before loosening the bolts joining the halves of a wheel, it is critically important that you

_____.

17. To safely insure complete deflation of a tire, first use a _____ _____ screwed onto the _____, then

remove the _____ _____.

18. Screwdrivers or tire tools _____ (should or should not) be used to pry a tire bead away from the rim.

19. Aircraft bearings _____(should or should not) be cleaned with steam.

20. Water stains on a wheel bearing is cause for rejection, because this may be an indication of

_____ corrosion.

21. Discolored bearings indicate damage due to _____.

22. Dye penetrant inspection _____(is or is not) a good method to use to locate cracks in the

bead seat area of an aircraft wheel.

23. _____ _____ inspections should be used to detect cracks on the bead seat area.

24. Wheel bolts should be inspected using the _____ _____

inspection method.

25. If _____(how many) of the fusible plugs in the wheel show any signs of softening, they

must all be replaced.

26. A(n) _____ _____ is used to reduce the back and forth

oscillations of the nose wheel at certain speeds.

27. If the front sides of the wheels of an aircraft are closer together than the rear sides, the landing gear is

_____(toed-in or toed-out).

28. If the tops of the wheels of an aircraft are closer together than the bottoms, the landing gear has a

_____(positive or negative) camber.

29. Large aircraft use a system to apply the brakes when the landing gear is selected UP in order to prevent a _____

hazard or possible _____ to the aircraft due to spinning wheels.

30. All retractable landing gear systems must have some means of _____(raising, lowering

or raising and lowering) the gear if the primary method fails.

31. Among the methods emergency gear extension systems may use are:

    a. _____

    b. _____

    c. _____

    d. _____

32. A(n) _____ switch may be installed in a landing gear retraction system to prevent the landing gear from being raised while the aircraft is on the ground.

33. Retractable gear aircraft generally use a _____ (what color) light to indicate that the gear is down and _____.

34. A gear warning horn will sound if the throttles are _____ (advanced or retarded) and _____(any or all) of the landing gear are in the up position.

35. Landing gear warning systems are designed to warn the pilot that the gear _____ (is or is not) down and locked when the aircraft is in the _____ configuration.

SECTION B
AIRCRAFT BRAKES

1. Metallic brake linings are also known as _____ linings.

2. Power brakes are operated using pressure from the _____ hydraulic system.

3. The hydraulic pressure to the brake system is reduced using a(n) _____ system.

4. A(n) _____ _____ valve is designed to prevent a complete loss of hydraulic system fluid if a brake line fails or leaks.

5. In case of total failure of the hydraulic system, most large aircraft brake systems can be operated using a(n) _____ emergency system.

6. The amount the automatic adjuster pin protrudes from the cylinder head of a Goodyear single-disk brake may be used as an indicator of the wear on the _____(linings or disk).

7. Cleveland brake linings should be replaced when they have worn to a thickness of _____ inch.

8. _____ brake action is nearly always an indication of air in the brake hydraulics system.

9. The operation performed to remove air from the brake system is known as _____ the

    brakes.

10. When bleeding air from a master cylinder brake system using the pressure method, the fresh fluid is introduced at

    the _____(wheel cylinder or reservoir).

11. If a brake system is inadvertently serviced with the wrong type of hydraulic fluid what must be accomplished?

    a. _____

    b. _____

12. Stopping a leaking MS-type flareless fitting by tightening the fitting _____ (is or is not) a proper repair

    procedure.

13. During brake overhaul the housings should be checked using the _____

    _____ inspection method.

14. It _____(is or is not) necessary to remove the wheel to replace the linings on a Cleveland

    single-disk brake.

15. Anytime a brake shows signs of _____, it must be removed from the aircraft, inspected,

    and rebuilt.

16. When a brake fails to completely release after the pressure is removed, it is said to be

    _____.

SECTION C
AIRCRAFT TIRES AND TUBES

1. The most popular low-pressure tire found on piston-powered aircraft today is the Type _____ tire.

2. The size of a low-pressure tire for piston powered aircraft is designated by the section _____ and rim

    _____.

3. The size of a high-pressure tire for jet aircraft is designated by the _____ _____ and the

    section _____.

4. The ply rating _____(does or does not) indicate the actual number of fabric plies in the

    tire.

5. Tubeless tires are identified by the word _____ on their sidewall.

6. Aircraft tire sidewalls are designed to deflect _____ (more or less) than automobile tires.

7. The most important part of a tire is the _____.

8. The most popular tread pattern found on aircraft tires today is the _____ tread.

9. A tire with a chine, or deflector, on its sidewall is used on the _____ (nose or main) wheel.

10. Heat is the greatest enemy of aircraft tires and _____ (externally or internally) generated heat is most likely to cause damage that results in tire failure.

11. The greatest heat will be generated in a tire that is operated _____ (under-inflated or over-inflated).

12. _____ (Over-inflation or Under-inflation) is most likely to result in tire damage or failure.

13. Identify the inflation condition that has caused the wear pattern on each of these aircraft tire sections:

A. _____   B. _____

C. _____.

14. The most important aspect of tire preventive maintenance is maintaining proper _____

_____.

15. The inflation pressure specified by the _____ (tire or airframe) manufacturer should be used to determine the proper inflation of a tire.

16. Air pressure should be checked when the tire is _____ (hot or cold).

17. Retreading _____ (is or is not) an acceptable procedure for aircraft tires.

18. Cracks in the sidewall rubber that expose the body cords of the tire _____ (are or are not) cause for rejection of the tire.

19. A(n) _____ (what type) seal is used between the halves of a wheel using a tubeless tire?

20. If the bead area of a tire is damaged, the tire _____(may or cannot) be repaired.

21. There _____(is or is not) a limit on the number of times an aircraft tire can be retreaded.

22. Ozone _____(is or is not) harmful to rubber products.

23. Tires should be stored _____(vertically or horizontally) whenever possible.

24. The two primary causes for an aircraft tube leaking are:

    a. _____

    b. _____

25. If a tube is suspected of leaking, first check the _____.

26. The red dot on an aircraft tire generally indicates the _____ (light or heavy) spot.

27. Wheel half bolts usually require a(n) _____ compound to be applied to the threads.

28. Before a tube is installed, the tube and the inside of the tire are dusted with approved _____ _____.

29. The yellow mark on an aircraft tube usually indicates the _____ (light or heavy) point.

30. Tires should always be inflated _____ (slowly or rapidly) inside a _____

    _____.

31. Three ways of attaching balance weights to an aircraft wheel are:

    a. _____

    b. _____

    c. _____

32. _____ is the controlled movement of the airplane under its own power, while on the

    ground.

33. While taxiing an airplane, if there is any doubt about clearance from an obstacle, _____ the airplane and

    _____.

34. _____ occurs when the aircraft's tires lose contact with the taxiway or runway surface,

    generally because of standing water on the surface.

POSITION AND WARNING SYSTEMS

SECTION A
ANTISKID BRAKE CONTROL SYSTEMS

1. If a locked wheel is not quickly released, the tire is likely to _____, causing aircraft _____ or

    loss of _____.

2. The braking effectiveness of a skidding tire is nearly _____.

3. To achieve maximum braking, the wheel should just start to _____ but not _____.

4. To achieve maximum braking and to stop the aircraft in the shortest possible distance, the pilot depresses the brake

    pedals _____.

5. Anti-skid systems typically deactivate automatically at about _____ MPH.

6. An auto-brake system automatically applies the brakes when the system senses _____ on the

    _____.

7. The three principal components of an anti-skid system are the:

    a. _____

    b. _____

    c. _____

8. An AC wheel speed sensor produces a variable frequency _____ while a DC wheel speed sensor

    produces a variable _____.

9. The control valve maintains an output _____, which is proportional to the signal

    _____ from the control unit.

10. Three main functions of the control unit are to:

    a. _____

    b. _____

    c. _____

11. A(n) _____-_____ detector prevents the pilot from landing with the brakes applied.

12. On wet or icy runways, the locked-wheel detector prevents a wheel from _____.

13. Anti-skid systems include _____ circuits and controls to verify proper operation.

14. The most logical place to begin troubleshooting an anti-skid system is with the

    _____.

SECTION B
INDICATING AND WARNING SYSTEMS

1. A stall occurs when an airplane reaches a critical _____ of _____.

2. Two types of stall warning used in small aircraft are:

    a. _____

    b. _____

3. Many stall warning systems measure the movement of the _____ _____ on the wing.

4. High performance aircraft generally use a _____-_____ to warn the pilot of an impending stall.

5. Angle-of-attack sensors may use either a _____ or a _____ type probe.

6. An Autosyn® position indicating system uses a pair of identical _____ motors in the

    transmitter and indicator.

7. A Magnesyn® system uses a _____ _____ rotor while an Autosyn® system uses an

    _____ rotor.

8. Arming a takeoff configuration warning system requires two conditions to be met. These conditions are:

    a. The aircraft is _____.

    b. One or more thrust levers is (are) _____.

9. A typical landing gear warning system uses one or more _____ lights to indicate a down-and-locked

    condition and a _____ light to indicate an unsafe condition.

10. Landing gear warning horns typically indicate that the aircraft is in _____ configuration with the gear

    not _____ and _____.

11. Mach airspeed warning can only be silenced by _____.

12. A _____ alerts the pilot of close proximity to terrain.

13. Critical engine parameters are monitored in new generation aircraft and presented on electronic displays by a(n)

    _____ _____ and _____ _____ system.

14. EICAS systems monitor both engine and airplane systems and display one of three types of messages when

abnormal conditions are detected. These are _____, _____ or _____ messages.

AIRCRAFT INSTRUMENT SYSTEMS

CHAPTER 11

SECTION A
PRINCIPLES OF INSTRUMENT SYSTEMS

1. Pressure may be measured in three ways. These are:

    a. _____ pressure.

    b. _____ pressure.

    c. _____ pressure.

2. Under standard day conditions, atmospheric pressure is _____ inches of Mercury or _____ psi.

3. An aneroid barometer measures _____ (absolute or gauge) pressure.

4. The difference between atmospheric pressure and the pressure being measured is called _____-pressure.

5. A(n) _____ type instrument is used to measure high pressures.

6. The two pressures sensed by the airspeed indicator are:

    a. _____

    b. _____

7. The manifold pressure gauge measures the _____ (absolute or gauge) pressure inside the induction system of a reciprocating engine.

8. The instrument that measures the differential pressure between the tailpipe total pressure and the compressor inlet total pressure of a turbine engine is the _____ _____ _____ indicator.

9. The _____ measures the absolute pressure of the air surrounding the aircraft.

10. The altitude shown on an altimeter when the local altimeter setting is placed in the barometric window is called _____ altitude.

11. All elevations on aeronautical charts are measured from _____ _____ _____.

12. The scale in the barometric window of an altimeter may be calibrated in _____ of _____ or

    _____.

13. The altitude shown on an altimeter when standard sea level pressure is put into the barometric window is called

    _____ altitude.

14. Flight level 320 is a pressure altitude of _____ feet.

15. Pressure altitude may be converted into density altitude by correcting the pressure altitude for non-standard

    _____.

16. Density altitude _____ (is or is not) a direct measurement.

17. When static ports are exposed to disturbed air, the results are altimeter system errors known as _____

    error.

18. Radio altimeters provide an indication of the aircraft's _____ altitude above

    _____ (sea level or ground level)

19. The tests required for a static system of an aircraft operated under instrument flight rules is described in FAR Part

    _____.

20. Altimeters installed in aircraft that operate under instrument flight rules must have their accuracy checked every

    _____ (how many) calendar months.

21. The uncorrected reading of an airspeed indicator is called _____ airspeed.

22. For navigation and flight planning purposes, a pilot is most interested in _____ (calibrated or true)

    airspeed.

23. An instrument that measures aircraft speed relative to the speed of sound is called a

    _____.

24. Mach _____ is flight at an airspeed of 95% of the speed of sound.

25. The rate-of-climb indicator is more properly known as the _____

    _____ indicator.

26. A vertical speed indicator measures the rate of change of _____ (pitot or static) pressure.

27. Resistance change-type temperature measuring instruments may use either a(n) _____

    _____ or a(n) _____ circuit.

28. A(n) _____ instrument is typically used to measure high temperatures.

29. It _____ (is or is not) permissible to cut off excess length of thermocouple leads.

30. An _____ gives the pilot an indication of the load imposed on the aircraft structure in terms of G's.

31. The _____ is used by the pilot of a twin-engine aircraft to synchronize the propeller rotations.

32. A(n) _____ - is an instrument that displays engine RPM.

33. The two basic characteristics of a gyroscope that makes it useful as a flight instrument are:

    a. _____

    b. _____

34. An attitude gyro uses the gyroscopic characteristic of _____.

35. The artificial horizon indicator senses rotation of an aircraft about which two of its axes?

    a. _____.

    b. _____.

36. The turn and slip indicator senses rotation about the _____ (which axis) axis of the aircraft.

37. A rate gyro uses the gyroscopic characteristic of _____.

38. The turn and slip indicator is actually two instruments in one housing, the non gyroscopic instrument is called a(n) _____.

39. Because navigation charts are laid out according to the geographic poles and a magnetic compass points to the magnetic poles, the difference between the positions is called _____.

40. Lines of equal variation on aeronautical charts are called _____ lines.

41. The line of zero variation is known as the _____ line.

42. Compass _____(deviation or variation) is caused by the magnetic fields in the aircraft that interfere with those of the earth.

43. Swinging a compass compensates for _____ (deviation or variation).

44. Two magnetic compass errors that a pilot must compensate for while in flight are _____ error and _____ error.

45. A _____ gyro combines a directional gyro with direction-sensing instrumentation.

46. Two major disadvantages to venturi systems for driving flight instruments are:

    a. _____

    b. _____

47. The rotor vanes of a dry-type vacuum pump are made of _____(carbon or steel).

48. Air-driven gyroscopic instruments require very _____ air.

49. An A&P maintenance technician _____ (can or cannot) disassemble and repair an aircraft instrument.

50. Three instruments that are connected to the static system are:

    a. _____

    b. _____

    c. _____

51. To prevent ice from obstructing a pitot tube, _____ (what type) heaters are used.

52. The alternate source valve in the aircraft flight instrument system is in the _____(pitot or

    static) system.

53. Direct current electrical fuel quantity indicators use a variable _____ as a tank unit, or

    sender.

54. The dielectric value of air is _____.

55. The dielectric value of fuel is approximately _____, but varies according to its

    temperature.

56. In a capacitance type fuel quantity indicating system the two dielectric materials used are _____ and

    _____.

57. Fuel pressure is typically measured in _____.

58. The mass type flowmeter is the _____(most or least) accurate method of measuring fuel

    flow.

59. What is meant by each of these sets of letters?

    a. EFIS _____

    b. CRT _____

    c. EADI _____

    d. ARINC _____

    e. EHSI _____

60. Greenwich mean time is also known as _____ time.

SECTION B
INSTRUMENT SYSTEM INSTALLATION AND MAINTENANCE PRACTICES

1. In which position in the basic T configuration for flight instruments are each of these instruments placed?

    a. _____ Altimeter

    b. _____ Attitude gyro

    c. _____ Directional gyro

    d. _____ Airspeed indicator

2. Shock mounts are used to isolate instruments and equipment from

    _____ (high frequency, low amplitude or low

    frequency, high amplitude) vibration.

3. A shock-mounted instrument panel must be electrically _____ (bonded or grounded) to the aircraft

    structure to provide a current _____ path.

4. Provide each of the instrument range markings and color codes for the following conditions represented on an

    airspeed indicator.

    a. Never-exceed speed _____

    b. Flap operating speed _____

    c. Caution area _____

    d. Best single-engine rate of climb speed _____

    e. Normal operating range _____

5. After completion of a static system test, it is critically important to ensure _____ of any material used to

    block the static ports.

6. A static system leak check is satisfactory if the altimeter drops no more than _____ feet in one minute.

AIRCRAFT AVIONICS SYSTEMS

CHAPTER 12

SECTION A

AVIONICS FUNDAMENTALS

1. Two types of fields exist in a radio transmitting antenna to cause it to radiate electrical energy. They are:

    a. _____

    b. _____

2. The higher the frequency, the _____ (longer or shorter) the wavelength.

3. The frequency of a radio transmission indicates the number of electromagnetic field

    _____ that occur in _____ second.

4. Each oscillation is called a _____ and frequency is measured in _____ per second or _____.

5. Radio waves travel at the speed of _____.

6. A(n) _____ wave is necessary to transmit radio waves and antennas are usually _____

    to _____ the length of the transmitted wave.

7. In order to transmit information, the _____ wave must be altered in some way and this alteration is

    called _____.

8. There are two ways a radio carrier wave may be modulated; these are:

    a. _____

    b. _____

9. _____ (What type) waves bounce off the ionosphere and can be used to achieve _____-

    _____ radio transmissions.

10. The three basic functions of every radio transmitter are:

    a. _____

    b. _____

    c. _____

11. The component that generates the carrier wave at the correct frequency is called a(n)

_____.

12. A component found in both transmitters and receivers whose function is to increase the strength of a signal is

called a(n) _____.

13. The length of a transmitting antenna is determined by the frequency (wavelength) for which the antenna is used.

The higher the frequency, the _____(shorter or longer) the antenna.

14. A half-wave antenna may also be referred to as a(n) _____ antenna.

15. The metal surrounding the base of a Marconi monopole antenna is called the

_____.

16. Aircraft VHF communications antennas are _____ (horizontally or vertically) polarized.

17. A(n) _____ circuit is used to isolate the desired frequency from all the frequencies intercepted by an

antenna.

18. High Frequency (HF) radios are most commonly used by large aircraft for _____ (general,

oceanic or continental) Air Traffic Control communications.

19. Most civilian aviation radio communication is done in the _____(UHF or VHF)

frequency range.

20. VHF communications and navigation equipment _____ (is or is not) limited to an operating

distance equivalent to the line of sight distance.

21. SATCOM radios operate in the _____ (VHF or UHF) frequency range and can carry both _____

and _____ communications.

22. A special VHF/HF communications system for calling a single, specific air carrier aircraft is known as

_____.

23. ACARS is a system for transmitting routine operational, maintenance and administrative messages to airliners via

a _____.

24. ADF refers to the _____ (airborne or ground) equipment and NDB refers to the associated

_____ (airborne or ground) equipment.

25. ADF operates in the _____(LF/MF or VHF/UHF) frequency range.

26. The two antennas required for the operation of an ADF are:

    a. _____

    b. _____

27. VOR operates in the _____(VHF or UHF) frequency range.

28. VOR is a _____(phase or voltage) comparison system.

29. VOR navigation radios used for IFR operations must be checked for accuracy every _____ days.

30. Distance measuring equipment _____(is or is not) a form of pulse equipment.

31. The principal advantage of an area navigation system is that it allows a pilot to fly

    _____.

32. An RNAV must be tuned to a _____(VOR or VORTAC) station to operate properly.

33. Inertial navigation systems _____(do or do not) require an external radio signal.

34. INS systems operate by very accurate measurement of _____ forces.

35. GPS is a _____ (ground or space)-based navigation system.

36. In order to determine an aircraft's position and altitude, the GPS system must receive a minimum of

    _____ signals.

37. It is possible for a pilot to respond with any of _____(how many) codes on a mode A/3

    radar beacon transponder.

38. Altitude information is transmitted from a radar beacon transponder when it is operating in Mode

    _____(A or C).

39. If two aircraft with operational Mode S transponders and _____ systems are on a collision course, the

    systems communicate with each other and present each pilot with guidance to _____

    _____.

40. Transponders must be tested and inspected every _____ calendar months.

41. The four ground-based components of the ILS are:

    a. _____

    b. _____

    c. _____

    d. _____

42. The glide-slope transmitter operates in the _____ (VHF or UHF) frequency range.

43. Tuning to the desired localizer frequency automatically tunes the _____ (marker beacon

    or glide slope) receiver to the proper frequency.

44. A marker beacon uses a single-frequency transmitter with a(n) _____ carrier frequency.

45. The amber light on the marker beacon receiver will light up when the aircraft passes over the

    _____ (outer or middle) marker.

46. An emergency locator transmitter is designed to transmit for _____ hours and operates on _____ MHz

    and _____ MHz.

47. Cockpit Voice Recorders and Flight Data Recorders are normally installed in the _____

    (forward or aft) fuselage area.

48. Basic weather radar signals are reflected only by the _____ (clouds or rain) inside the

    storm.

49. Fill in the color that is used on a color weather radar to indicate the intensity of the rainfall:

    a. Least severe _____

    b. Medium severity _____

    c. Most severe _____

50. _____ (X-band or C-band) radar is more common in general aviation airplanes.

51. _____ (X-band or C-band) radar is better for penetrating known areas of precipitation.

52. A Stormscope detects the radio waves emitted by _____.

53. A major disadvantage of TCAS systems is that they cannot detect aircraft that do not have operating

    _____.

SECTION B
AUTOPILOTS AND FLIGHT DIRECTORS

1. The primary function of an autopilot is to relieve the pilot's need to _____ _____

   the aircraft.

2. A single-axis autopilot usually operates only the _____.

3. A two-axis autopilot normally controls the _____ and the _____.

4. AFCS systems on jet transports may have both auto-_____ and auto-_____

   capability.

5. The latest, most sophisticated autopilots are called _____ _____

   _____.

6. Flight Management Computers can automatically control a flight from just after _____ to _____ and _____.

7. Modern autopilots use _____ gyros or _____ gyros to generate error signals.

8. The device used by an autopilot to actuate a control surface is called a _____.

9. Two major advantages of ring laser gyros are that they don't:

    a. _____

    b. _____

10. Small aircraft autopilots may use _____ servos or _____ servos.

11. Flight directors calculate flight path corrections and _____ (a or b).

    a. Actuate servos to maneuver the airplane.

    b. Display a command for the pilot to follow.

SECTION C
INSTALLATION AND MAINTENANCE OF AVIONICS

1. Avionics equipment requires good _____ _____ connections for proper operation.

2. Avionics equipment _____ (is or is not) easily damaged by heat.

3. Wiring should be routed _____ lines that carry fluids and _____ securely to the aircraft structure.

4. Avionics equipment should be turned off during engine starting and shutdown to prevent damage from _____ currents and voltage _____.

5. Aircraft switches must be of the _____ - _____ type.

6. Aircraft circuit breakers must be of the _____ - _____ type.

7. Bonding jumpers should have an electrical resistance of no more than _____ ohms.

8. The component of an avionics system that captures electromagnetic interference generated by an ignition system and sends it to ground is called _____.

9. Static _____, also called static _____ are usually located on the _____ edges of primary control surfaces and discharge static electricity to the _____.

10. _____(what type) antenna cable is constructed of a center conductor surrounded by a

dielectric, which is surrounded by a shield or outer conductor and that is surrounded by an outer protective

insulator.

11. Antenna cables should be replaced if they are _____, _____,

_____, _____, or have _____ wire braid.

AIRFRAME ICE AND RAIN CONTROL

CHAPTER 13

SECTION A
AIRFRAME ICE CONTROL SYSTEMS

1. Only aircraft that are specially equipped and properly certified may fly into _____ icing conditions.

2. The formation of ice is prevented by _____ (anti-icing or deicing) systems.

3. Ice is removed from aircraft surfaces by _____(anti-icing or deicing) systems.

4. Frost must be removed from the wings of an airplane before flight because it forms an effective aerodynamic _____ on the surface, and increases drag.

5. There _____(does or does not) have to be visible water in the air for carburetor ice to form.

6. Turbine powered aircraft may use _____ air to heat the leading edges of the wings to prevent the formation of ice.

7. The inlet guide vanes on a turbine engine are provided with anti-icing protection from _____(bleed air or electrical current).

8. Pitot heads are protected from icing with _____(hot air or electrical heaters).

9. If there is no provision for ice removal on the static port, the aircraft should be equipped with an _____ air source valve.

10. Windshields are normally _____ (electrically or pneumatically) heated to prevent ice from obstructing the flight crew's vision.

11. An aircraft windshield has a greater bird-impact resistance when it is _____(heated or cold).

12. The three types of anti-icing systems are:

    a. _____

    b. _____

    c. _____

13. Chemical anti-icing systems may be found on these components:

  a. _____

  b. _____

  c. _____

14. Propeller anti-icing systems normally use _____ alcohol to prevent icing.

15. When the tubes in deicer boots are deflated, they are held tightly against the wing by

    _____.

16. The air to inflate rubber deicer boots installed on an airplane powered by a reciprocating engine is taken from the

    discharge of the _____ pump.

17. Two ways of securing rubber deicer boots to the leading edge of a wing are:

  a. _____

  b. _____

18. The surfaces of rubber deicer boots should be kept clean by periodically washing them with a solution of

    _____ and _____.

19. Propellers are normally deiced with _____(hot air or electrothermal boots).

20. Electrical current is supplied to the propeller deicers using _____ and

    _____ assemblies.

21. Electric propeller deicers operate _____(continuously or on a sequenced cycle).

22. The length of time that a deiced surface will be protected from ice, snow or frost is called

    _____ time.

23. Aircraft should be deiced as closed to _____ time as possible, especially if bad weather

    conditions are likely to reduce _____ time.

24. Hard or sharp tools _____ (may or may not) be used to scrape or chip ice from the surface of an

    airplane.

25. Frost may be removed from an aircraft on the ground by spraying it with a mixture of

    _____ _____ and _____

    _____.

SECTION B
RAIN CONTROL SYSTEMS

1. Large aircraft may use one of three methods of rain control. They are:

    a. _____

    b. _____

    c. _____

2. Two methods of operating aircraft windshield wipers are:

    a. _____

    b. _____

3. Operating windshield wipers on a dry windshield _____ (is or is not) permissible.

4. Chemical rain repellent should be used only in a _____ (heavy or light) rain.

5. Pneumatic rain removal systems use _____ air from the engine.

CABIN ATMOSPHERE CONTROL SYSTEMS

CHAPTER 14

SECTION A
FLIGHT PHYSIOLOGY

1. Express the standard sea level conditions of our atmosphere:

    a. Sea level pressure = _____ pounds per square inch.

    b. Sea level pressure = _____ inches of mercury.

    c. Sea level temperature = _____ degrees Fahrenheit.

    d. Sea level temperature = _____ degrees Celsius.

2. The two most abundant elements in our atmosphere are:

    a. _____

    b. _____

3. Anytime a person's body is deprived of oxygen he or she will develop _____.

4. When the brain is deprived of oxygen, a person's _____ and _____ are impaired.

5. _____ is the product of incomplete combustion, and is found in varying amounts in the smoke and fumes from burning aviation fuels.

6. Some form of supplemental oxygen is normally recommended for flight above _____ feet.

SECTION B
OXYGEN AND PRESSURIZATION SYSTEMS

1. Pure oxygen _____ (will or will not) burn.

2. Aircraft oxygen systems should never be serviced with any oxygen that is not labeled _____ _____ Oxygen.

3. Almost all military aircraft now carry oxygen in its _____ (solid, liquid, or gaseous) state.

4.   Mechanically-separated oxygen systems produce oxygen by drawing air through a patented material called a(n)

_____ _____.

5.   High pressure oxygen cylinders should be painted _____(green or yellow).

6.   What DOT approval codes should appear on steel aircraft oxygen cylinders?

     a. _____

     b. _____

7.   Type 3AA oxygen cylinders must be hydrostatically tested to _____ (what amount) of their working pressure

every _____ years.

8.   The two types of continuous flow oxygen regulators are:

     a. _____

     b. _____

9.   The oxygen regulator used by the flight crews of most commercial jet airliners are of the

_____(continuous flow or diluter-demand) -type.

10. A rebreather bag type mask is used with a _____ (continuous flow, diluter-demand or

pressure-demand)-type regulator.

11. The oxygen masks that automatically drop from the overhead compartment of a jet transport aircraft are of the

_____ (continuous flow or demand)-type.

12. Most of the rigid plumbing lines that carry high-pressure oxygen are made of _____

_____.

13. Liquid oxygen systems are referred to using the initials _____.

14. The pressure of the oxygen delivered to the regulator by a liquid oxygen converter is usually

_____psi.

15. _____ _____(what chemical) mixed with appropriate binders

and a fuel is used to make oxygen candles.

16. A chemical oxygen candle _____ (does or does not) generate heat.

17. Oxygen candles have a _____(short or long) shelf life.

18. Once ignited, a chemical oxygen candle _____ (can or cannot) be extinguished.

19. When a nitrogen cylinder is installed on the oxygen servicing cart it will face the

_____(same or opposite) direction of the oxygen cylinders.

20. An oxygen system is considered to be empty when the pressure gets down to _____ to

    _____psi.

21. When servicing an aircraft oxygen system from a service cart having several cylinders, always start with the

    cylinder having the _____(lowest or highest) pressure.

22. Refer to the oxygen servicing chart on page 14-18 [Figure 14-21] in the *Jeppesen A&P Technician Airframe Text*.

    With an outside air temperature of 30°F. an oxygen system must be filled to _____ psi to

    obtain a stabilized pressure of 1,800 psi at 70°F.

23. During oxygen servicing there should be no smoking, open flame, or items which may cause sparks within

    _____ feet or more.

24. Aircraft cabin pressurization is controlled by varying the amount of air that is

    _____(taken in or allowed to leak out).

25. Smaller reciprocating engine aircraft may obtain air for cabin pressurization from _____

    _____ bleed air.

26. Most pressurization systems have what three cockpit indicators?

    a. _____

    b. _____

    c. _____

27. The two modes of operation for cabin pressurization are:

    a. _____

    b. _____

28. The _____(outflow or safety) valve is controlled by the cabin altitude controller.

SECTION C
CABIN CLIMATE CONTROL SYSTEMS

1. The most common type of heater for small single-engine aircraft is the _____

   _____ heater.

2. Light- and medium-twin engine aircraft are often heated with _____ heaters.

3. The thermostat of a combustion heater controls the _____ (fuel valve or ignition).

4. The ventilating air pressure inside the combustion heater is _____(higher or lower) than the pressure of the combustion air.

5. When the temperature is reached for which the duct limit switch of a combustion heater is set, the

_____(fuel or ignition) to the heater is shut off.

6. Which of these controls for a combustion heater is not normally accessible in flight?

_____(a, b, or c)

    a. Heater master switch.

    b. Cabin thermostat.

    c. Overheat switch.

7. Two methods of removing heat from the air in an air cycle air conditioning system are:

    a. _____

    b. _____

8. The water separator in an air cycle air conditioning system removes the water from the air

_____(before or after) it passes through the air cycle machine.

9. Two types of air conditioning system for lowering the temperature of the air in an aircraft cabin are:

    a. _____

    b. _____

10. Heat that is added to a liquid that causes a change in its state without changing its temperature is called

_____ heat.

11. The two components in a vapor cycle air conditioning system that divide the system into the high and low side are

the:

    a. _____

    b. _____

12. The component in a vapor cycle air conditioning system that acts as the reservoir for the refrigerant is the

_____.

13. The substance in a vapor cycle air conditioning system that is found in the receiver-dryer and used to remove

moisture from the refrigerant is known as _____.

14. The component in a vapor cycle air conditioning system in which heat from the cabin is absorbed into the

refrigerant is the _____.

15. The refrigerant most generally used in aircraft air-conditioning systems is _____(R-12 or R-22).

16. The thermal expansion valve of a vapor cycle air conditioning system is the _____ device for the system.

17. The component in a vapor cycle air conditioning system in which the heat in the refrigerant is given up to the outside air is the _____.

18. Two types of leak detectors that are suitable for detecting a refrigerant leak in an aircraft air conditioning system are:

   a. _____

   b. _____

19. If bubbles are visible in the _____ _____ there is not enough refrigerant in the system.

20. Any time a vapor cycle air conditioning system has been opened, it must be _____ before it is recharged.

21. Refrigerant should normally be put into the low side of an air conditioning system in its _____(liquid or vapor) state.

CHAPTER 15

AIRCRAFT FUEL SYSTEMS

SECTION A
AVIATION FUELS AND FUEL SYSTEM REQUIREMENTS

1. Water in a fuel system _____ (will or will not) cause the engine(s) to stop.

2. If jet fuel is introduced into a turbocharged piston engine fuel system, it will cause severe

    _____, which can lead to _____.

3. The two most widely used aviation fuels are _____ and

    _____.

4. The density of jet fuel varies _____ (more or less) than that of avgas with variations in temperature.

5. The measure of the tendency of a liquid to vaporize under given conditions is known as

    _____.

6. Detonation may also be known as engine _____.

7. When considering aviation fuel performance numbers, the first number indicates the

    _____(rich or lean)-mixture rating.

8. Current practice is to designate grades by the lean performance number ratings. The three grades of aviation

    gasoline in current use are designated as:

    a. _____

    b. _____

    c. _____

9. What color dye is used to identify each of these aviation gasolines:

    a. Avgas 80 _____

    b. Avgas 100 _____

    c. 100LL _____

10. The three types of turbine fuel currently being used are:

    a. _____

    b. _____

    c. _____

11. Water occurs in aviation fuel in what two forms?

    a. _____

    b. _____

12. The most effective method to limit microbial growths in turbine fuel is to eliminate _____

    from the fuel.

13. The common forms of aviation fuel contaminants are:

    a. _____

    b. _____

    c. _____

    d. _____

    e. _____

14. It _____(is or is not) permissible for a fuel pump to draw fuel from more than one tank at a

    time.

15. A gravity-feed fuel system must be able to flow at least _____%(what percent) of the

    takeoff fuel flow.

16. A pump-feed fuel system must be able to flow at least _____%(what percent) of the

    takeoff fuel flow.

17. Each fuel tank must have a(n) _____%(what percent) expansion space.

18. If the design landing weight of an aircraft is less than the permitted takeoff weight a fuel

    _____ system must be provided.

SECTION B
FUEL SYSTEM OPERATION

1. Low wing aircraft _____(can or cannot) use gravity to feed fuel to the carburetor.

2. An electric boost pump is used for these three operations:

    a. _____.

    b. _____.

    c. _____.

3. Three types of aircraft fuel tanks are:

    a. _____

    b. _____

    c. _____

4. Welded aluminum fuel tanks are usually made of _____ or _____

    aluminum alloy.

5. Welded or riveted fuel tanks may be sealed by pouring a liquid sealant into the tank and allowing it to cover the

    entire inside of the tank. The surplus is poured out, and that which remains is allowed to cure. This method of

    sealing is called _____ the tank.

6. A(n) _____ fuel tank consists of part of the aircraft structure that has been sealed to

    contain the fuel.

7. A fuel bay that holds a bladder tank must have all of the edges of the metal and all of the rivets and screw heads

    covered with _____ _____ tape.

8. If a bladder-type fuel tank is to be left empty for an extended period of time, the inside of the tank should be coated

    with a film of _____ _____.

9. A fuel tank cap that has a "goose neck" tube over the vent must be installed so the opening in the tube faces

    _____ (forward or rearward).

10. Most of the rigid fuel lines used in aircraft are made of _____ aluminum alloy, or

    _____ steel.

11. A flareless fitting in a fuel line must be tightened no more than one-_____ to one-

    _____ of a turn after the fitting is finger tight.

12. The _____ line of a flexible hose will indicate if the hose has been installed with a twist.

13. If an electrical wire bundle and a fuel line are run parallel through a compartment of an aircraft, the electrical wire

    bundle should be installed _____ (above or below) the fuel line.

14. "All runs of rigid tubing installed between fittings in an aircraft fuel system should have at least one bend in them."

    This statement is _____ (true or false).

15. Hand operated fuel valves found on small and medium sized aircraft will likely be one of these types:

    a. _____

    b. _____

16. A device that gives a fuel valve a positive feel when it is in the full ON or full OFF position is called a(n)

    _____.

17. Two methods of actuating remotely operated fuel valves are by _____ _____ or by

    _____.

18. A wobble pump is a _____(single or double) -acting pump.

19. The most popular type of auxiliary fuel pump is the _____ boost pump.

20. A centrifugal boost pump is used in its _____(low or high) -speed position for supplying

    the fuel required to start the engine.

21. A fuel ejector system uses the _____ principle to supply additional fuel to the collector

    can.

22. Pulsating-type electric fuel pumps are installed _____(in series or parallel) with the

    engine-driven fuel pump.

23. A vane-type pump is a _____(constant or variable) displacement pump.

24. If a vane-type pump is installed in an airplane as an auxiliary fuel pump, it is installed in

    _____(series or parallel) with the engine-driven fuel pump.

25. Two auxiliary valves that are built into a vane-type fuel pump are:

    a. _____

    b. _____

26. All fuel tanks should have a drain _____ or _____ at their lowest point.

27. If a fuel filter in a jet aircraft clogs because of dirt in the fuel, the flow of fuel to the engine

    _____(will or will not) be stopped.

28. When it is necessary to known the mass of the fuel in the tanks, a(n) _____ -type fuel

    quantity indicating system is used.

29. Reciprocating engines equipped with fuel injection systems may use a fuel flowmeter that is actually a fuel

    _____ gauge.

SECTION C
FUEL SYSTEM REPAIR, TESTING, AND SERVICING

1. Before any fuel tank is welded, it must be purged of all explosive fumes using _____ or

    some chemical compound.

2. Welded fuel tanks are normally tested with _____ psi of air pressure inside the tank.

3. Terneplate is used to manufacture some fuel tanks. It is sheet steel coated with _____ and

    _____.

4. Before repairing an integral fuel tank, it should be purged of all fuel vapors with either _____ or

    _____ _____.

5. When testing a repaired integral fuel tank, it should have no more than _____ psi air

    pressure put into the tank.

6. When classifying fuel leaks, the size of the surface area that a fuel leak moistens in a(n)

    _____ (how many) minute period is used.

7. Aircraft _____ (should or should not) be serviced with fuel in a hangar or other enclosed

    area.

8. The bleeding off of electrical charges on aircraft _____ (is or is not) an instantaneous act.

9. When connecting bonding cables between a refueler and an aircraft, you should connect the fueler to

    _____ (ground or aircraft) first.

10. The principle effects of micro organisms in turbine fuel are:

    a. _____

    b. _____

    c. _____

11. The _____ (what type) test is used to detect microscopic solid contaminants in turbine fuel.

12. If you are driving a fuel truck, you should approach the aircraft _____ (head-on or

    parallel) to the wings.

13. The most important safety consideration when fueling an aircraft is to be certain that only the _____

    _____ of fuel is put into the fuel tanks.

FIRE PROTECTION SYSTEMS

CHAPTER 16

SECTION A
FIRE DETECTION

1. For a fire to occur, there must be:

   a. _____

   b. _____

   c. _____

2. Name the NFPA class of fire that is described by each of these conditions:

   a. A fire in which there are energized electrical circuits is a class-_____ fire.

   b. A fire with liquid fuel is a class-_____ fire.

   c. A fire in which there is burning metal is a class-_____ fire.

   d. A fire with solid combustibles as the fuel is a class-_____ fire.

3. A wheel well or wing compartment would be considered to be a Class _____ fire zone.

4. The two general categories of engine fire detection systems are:

   a. _____ systems.

   b. _____ systems.

5. The thermal switch fire detection system is a(n) _____-type system.

6. Thermal switch fire detection units respond to a _____ (pre-set temperature or a rate-of-temperaure-rise).

7. Thermal switch fire detectors are connected in _____ (series or parallel) with each other.

8. A significant advantage of a double loop detection circuit is that it can withstand a _____ such as a _____ or _____ circuit without causing a false fire warning.

9. Thermocouple fire detection systems may also be known as the _____ fire detection system.

10. Thermocouple fire detection systems respond to a

    _____ (pre-set temperature or a rate-of-

    temperature-rise).

11. In the thermocouple system, one thermocouple called the _____ thermocouple is placed in

    a location that is relatively well protected from the initial flame.

12. The two relays in a thermocouple fire detection system are:

    a. _____

    b. _____

13. More complete coverage of a fire hazard area than is provided by a spot-detector system may be obtained using

    a(n) _____ _____ fire detection system.

14. The _____ (Fenwall or Kidde) continuous loop system uses two wires inside and inconel

    tube.

15. A _____ (sensor-responder or continuous loop) fire detection system may also function as

    an overheat indicator.

16. The two types of sensor-responder systems that may be found in use are the :

    a. _____ system.

    b. _____ system.

17. What two gases are toxic to humans, may indicate a fire condition and may provide the earliest warning of a

    dangerous situation?

    a. _____

    b. _____

18. _____ type smoke detectors use a small amount of radioactive material to ionize some of

    the oxygen and nitrogen drawn into the unit.

19. Three types of smoke detection units which may be found on aircraft are:

    a. _____

    b. _____

    c. _____

SECTION B
FIRE EXTINGUISHING SYSTEMS

1. Carbon dioxide _____ (is or is not) effective on Class B and Class C fires.

2. Halogenated hydrocarbons are identified through a system of _____ numbers.

3. Two typical inspection items for portable fire extinguishers are:

    a. _____

    b. _____

4. HRD extinguishing systems are discharged by an electrically ignited discharge cartridge called a

    _____.

5. If an installed fire extinguishing system has been discharged by normal operation the

    _____ (red or yellow) blowout disk will be ruptured.

6. Almost all type of fire extinguisher containers require _____ to determine the amount of

    extinguishing agent.

7. Fire extinguisher containers must be hydrostatically tested every _____ years.

8. If a discharge cartridge is removed from a discharge valve, it _____ (may or may not) be

    used in another discharge valve assembly.

AIRCRAFT AIRWORTHINESS INSPECTION

CHAPTER 17

SECTION A
AIRCRAFT AIRWORTHINESS INSPECTION

1. Inspection programs must ensure that an aircraft is _____ and conforms to all applicable FAA:

    a. _____

    b. _____

    c. _____

    d. _____

2. A(n) _____ is defined as the number of takeoffs and landings made by an aircraft.

3. Aircraft weighing less than 12,500 lbs gross takeoff weight have maintenance checklists that conform to FAR Part

    ____, Appendix __

4. During a pre-flight inspection, the pilot must verify that certain documents are aboard the aircraft. These

    documents are:

    a. _____

    b. _____

    c. _____

    d. _____

5. A Minimum Equipment List or MEL contains information on equipment that may be

    _____ and still allow the aircraft to fly for a specific time period.

6. Small airplanes are required to have an annual inspection every _____

    months.

7. If a small airplane is operated for compensation or hire, it must be inspected every _____ (what number)

    hours of operation in addition the annual inspection.

8. If a small airplane is inspected on May 1st, the annual inspection is good until _____ (what time) on

    _____ (what day) of the following year.

9. Detailed inspection checklists, meeting the requirements of FAR Part 43, Appendix D are provided by the

   _____ (FAA or Manufacturer)

10. An A & P Technician who does not hold an Inspection Authorization _____ (may or may not)

    perform an Annual Inspection.

11. If an airplane fails an annual inspection, the inspector must provide the owner with a list of _____

    and _____ items.

12. An A & P technician may correct discrepancies found during an Annual Inspection and approve the aircraft for

    return to service provided the discrepancy does not involve a _____ repair.

13. An unairworthy aircraft may not be flown to a different repair location unless a _____ _____

    _____ is obtained.

14. An aircraft requiring a 100-hour inspection may be operated for a maximum of _____ hours while enroute to an

    inspection facility.

15. An aircraft whose 100-hour inspection was due at 1,327 hours total time was flown for an additional 4 hours

    before the inspection was performed. The next 100-hour inspection is due at _____ hours total time.

16. A certified A & P technician _____ (may or may not) perform a 100-hour inspection and approve the

    aircraft for return to service.

17. The same inspection can serve as both a 100-hour and an annual inspection if the person performing the inspection

    holds an _____ _____.

18. A 100-hour inspection _____ (may or may not) take the place of an Annual inspection.

19. An inspection program that divides the Annual inspection into smaller blocks of work is called a

    _____ inspection schedule.

20. What types of aircraft require inspection programs tailored to the specific aircraft and its unique operating

    conditions?

    a. _____

    b. _____

21. A(n) _____ inspection compares the approved aircraft specifications with the actual aircraft,

    engine and components.

22. FAA Form _____ is used to record major repair and alteration information.

23. The _____ inspection is one of the most commonly overlooked or incompletely carried out

    procedures.

24. Air Carriers operating under Part 121 must maintain their aircraft under a _____ Airworthiness

    Maintenance Program.

25. CAMP inspection schedules are often called "_____ checks."

26. The control documents for a continuous inspection program are called _____ _____.

27. Part 135 operators usually choose to implement a(n) _____ Aircraft Inspection Program.

28. Aircraft operated under Instrument Flight Rules must have the altimeters and static systems inspected every _____

    calendar months.

29. ATC transponder inspections are one of a number of _____ (what type) inspections and are required

    every _____ _____ _____.

30. Emergency Locator Transmitter inspections are required every _____ calendar months.

31. A(n) _____ inspection is an unscheduled inspection conducted as a result of a specific over-

    limit or abnormal event.

SECTION B
INSPECTION GUIDELINES AND PROCEDURES

1. The five most common sources of aircraft wear and tear are:

    a. _____

    b. _____

    c. _____

    d. _____

    e. _____

2. Corrosion, oxidation, and rot or decay are examples of damage caused by _____.

3. Abrasion, burnishing, galling, and scoring are examples of damage caused by _____.

4. _____ (what type) overloads cause damage from tension, compression, torsion, shear, and bending.

5. Leaking baffles, improper cowl flap rigging and oil leaks may cause _____ heat damage.

6. Review of the aircraft maintenance records, airworthiness directive and service bulletin research and checklist

    preparation are part of the _____ phase.

7. A(n) _____ _____ is an agreement between the owner and the shop concerning the work to be

    performed.

8. The five basic phases of an aircraft inspection are:

    a. _____

    b. _____

    c. _____

    d. _____

    e. _____

9. Compliance with Airworthiness Directives (AD's) is _____ (optional or mandatory).

10. The actual inspection of the aircraft is referred to as the _____ phase.

11. When performing an annual or 100-hour inspection, FAR part 43.15 requires a _____ (flight or functional) check on the aircraft engines.

12. An aircraft cannot be returned to service after an inspection until the _____ is complete.

13. After maintenance or inspection, and prior to flight, entries must be made in the aircraft maintenance records and signed off by a(n) _____ _____ maintenance technician.

SECTION C
AIRCRAFT MAINTENANCE RECORDS

1. Missing or incomplete maintenance records _____ (will or will not) affect the airworthiness of an aircraft.

2. FAR Part _____ outlines maintenance entry requirements while FAR Part _____ outlines inspection entry content.

3. Records of maintenance, preventive maintenance, repairs or alterations to an aircraft, engine, propeller, appliance or component must contain:

    a. _____

    b. _____

    c. _____

    d. _____

    e. _____

    f. _____

4. The _____ (maintenance technician or owner) is responsible for maintaining records of the total time in service of an aircraft, engine, propeller or rotor.

5. For maintenance records, the time from the moment of takeoff to the moment of touchdown at the next point of landing is called _____ _____ _____ .

6. Records of compliance with AD's _____ (may or may not) be kept as a separate listing in the maintenance records.

ANSWERS

CHAPTER 1

AIRCRAFT STRUCTURAL ASSEMBLY AND RIGGING

SECTION 1A

1. truss
2. stressed-skin, monocoque
3. scmi-monocoque
4. semi-monocoque
5. fail-safe
6. attack
7. low
8. ribs
9. behind
10. truss
11. drag
12. cantilever
13. chemical, electrochemical
14. stiffness
15. ahead of
16. corrugating
17. a. ailerons
    b. rudder
    c. elevator
18. inboard
19. spoiler
20. performance, drag, wingtip vortices
21. Vortex generators
22. empennage
23. dorsal
24. stabilator
25. anti-servo
26. ruddervators
27. fuselage

28. Pratt
29. Warren
30. conventional
31. tricycle
32. parasite
33. pressure
34. fins
35. cowl flaps
36. open
37. a. beneath the wing
    b. at the rear fuselage

SECTION 1B

1. a. longitudinal, roll
   b. lateral, pitch
   c. vertical, yaw
2. longitudinal (roll)
3. lateral (pitch)
4. vertical (yaw)
5. rudder
6. a. static
   b. dynamic
7. a. longitudinal (pitch)
   b. lateral (roll)
   c. vertical (yaw)
8. stabilizer
9. elevators
10. downward
11. up
12. rearward
13. down
14. up
15. balance
16. aileron drag
17. up
18. Frise
19. interconnect springs
20. right
21. trim tab
22. opposite
23. anti-servo
24. same
25. opposite
26. high
27. jackscrew

28. down
29. drag
30. increase
31. slotted
32. Fowler
33. slot, aileron
34. a. hydraulically
    b. electrically
35. camber
36. root
37. at the wing root
38. vortices
39. high, low
40. Winglets
41. wing fence
42. canard
43. irreversible
44. a. ailerons
    b. flight spoilers
45. two
46. yaw damper
47. a. Kreuger flaps
    b. variable camber leading edge flaps
48. Type Certificatc Data Sheets
49. washed-out
50. droop
51. a. 1 X 7 or 1 X 19
    b. 7 X 7
    c. 7 X 19
52. a. 75%
    b. 100%
53. 60%
54. a. wear
    b. corrosion
55. may not
56. a. 92
    b. 52
    c. 70
    d. 25
57. three
58. four
59. is not
60. positive
61. decalage

62. landing
63. lower
64. cycle
65. a. metal fatigue
    b. corrosion
66. tests and inspection,
    aging aircraft program

SECTION 1C

1. autorotational
   (autorotative)
2. vertical tail rotor
3. a. fore & aft counter-
      rotating rotors
   b. co-axial counter-
      rotating rotors.
4. feather
5. a. gravity
   b. centrifugal force
   c. lift
   d. drag
6. symmetrical
7. a. rigidity in space
   b. precession
8. Precession
9. Coriolis effect
10. underslung
11. less than one diameter
12. Out of Ground Effect
13. In Ground Effect
14. advancing
15. forward
16. flap, feather
17. retreating
18. high
19. translational
20. autorotational
21. downward
22. upward
23. collective
24. correlator, governor
25. collective
26. cyclic
27. synchronized elevator
28. irreversible
29. pedals
30. fenestron
31. unstable
32. a. stabilizer bar
    b. offset flapping hinges
    c. stability
       augmentation
33. beat
34. low
35. vertical
36. lateral
37. a. statically
    b. dynamically

38. a. chordwise
    b. spanwise
39. a. marking stick or flag
    b. strobe light
    c. infrared light
40. on the ground
41. in-flight
42. fan
43. collective
44. a. direct-shaft
    b. free turbine
45. clutch
46. freewheeling

CHAPTER 2

SHEET METAL STRUCTURES

SECTION 2A

1. aluminum
2. a. monocoque
   b. semi-monocoque
3. a. strength
   b. stiffness
   c. shape
4. a. tension
   b. compression
   c. torsion
   d. bending
   e. shear
5. compressive
6. tensile
7. compression, tension
8. a. tensile (tension)
   b. shear
9. shear
10. concentrate, cross-
    sectional area
11. stop-drill
12. are
13. a. copper
    b. copper
    c. magnesium
    d. zinc
14. 1xxx
15. 2024
16. pure aluminum, rolled
17. scratches, abrasions
18. solution
19. precipitation
20. softened

21. a. –F
    b. –O
    c. –T4
    d. –T3
    e. –T6
    f. –H12
    g. –H18
22. lighter
23. a. cracks easily
    b. corrodes easily
    c. burns readily
24. strength, weight
25. high
    a. firewalls
    b. exhaust systems
26. a. high strength
    b. light weight
    c. stiffness
27. a. cladding with pure
       aluminum
    b. covering with an
       impenetrable oxide
       film
    c. covering with primer
       and paint
28. a. An area of electrode
       potential difference
    b. A conductive path
       between these areas.
    c. An electrolyte covering
       the surface
29. will not
30. a. electrolytically
    b. chemically

SECTION 2B

1. should not
2. should not, the part will
   crack when it is bent
3. Carbon infuses into the
   metal, which will cause the
   part to weaken and crack.
4. are
5. transfer
6. pin
7. nibbler
8. a. green
   b. red
   c. yellow
9. countersunk
10. squaring shear
11. a. tip
    b. body
    c. shank
12. 30
13. box
14. a. silver
    b. copper

  c. black
  d. brass
15. hole finder
16. chip chaser
17. 1/16th, 1/32nd
18. a. countersunk
  b. universal
  c. round
  d. flat
19. countersunk, dimpled
20. a. 1100
  b. 2117
  c. 2017
  d. 2024
  e. 5056
21. a. 1100
  b. 5056
  c. 2117
  d. 2017
  e. 2024
  f. 7050
22. B
23. heat treated, icebox
24. blind
25. rivnut
26. Dzus, Airloc, Camlock

SECTION 2C

1. 1 1/2
2. two
3. three, ten to twelve
4. 75%
5. a. #40
  b. #30
  c. #21
  d. #11
6. 100
7. coin
8. hot
9. one-shot
10. inside
11. a. three
  b. two
  c. one
12. across
13. a. 0
  b. 2-4t (.064"-.128")
  c. 4-6t (.256"-.384")
14. mold
15. setback
16. BR + MT
17. K-value or K-factor
18. (K) times (R+T)
19. a. 0.290"
  b. 0.120"
  c. 0.700"
  d. 0.625"
20. bend allowance

21. a. 0.420"
  b. 0.219"
  c. 0.328"
  d. 0.214"
  e. 0.196"
22. stretched
23. may
24. flanged
25. joggling

SECTION 2D

1. burnishing
2. Structural Repair
3. data, FAA approved
4. Inspection Authorization
5. 337
6. Provides a more gradual change for stresses to enter and leave the repair.
7. 1/8th (same size)
8. An aircraft grade bolt and self-locking nut.
9. inboard
10. Slip roll former.
11. wet
12. removing the damaged area and installing a new piece of skin.
13. add
14. location, approved
15. sealant

CHAPTER

3

WOOD, COMPOSITE, AND TRANSPARENT PLASTIC STRUCTURES

SECTION 3A

1. Sitka Spruce
2. a. cut of the wood
  b. slope of the grain
  c. number of growth rings
3. quarter, shrinkage
4. 1 to 15
5. a. Resorcinol glue
  b. Epoxy resin glue
6. should not

7. a. pot life
  b. open assembly time
  c. closed assembly time
  d. pressing time
8. Mahogany
9. lowest
10. rot-inhibiting
11. varnish
12. rotted
13. may not
14. 1/10th
15. 5:1

SECTION 3B

1. a. strength and stiffness can be customized
  b. high strength-to-weight ratio
  c. can be formed into complex curves
2. a. fiber
  b. matrix
  c. interface or boundary between elements
3. a. S-glass
  b. E-glass
4. Aramid
5. high stress, vibration
6. compressive, galvanic
7. ceramic
8. parallel
9. warp
10. selvage
11. bias
12. uni-directional
13. mats
14. more
15. a. thermoplastic
  b. thermosetting
16. little, must be
17. will, will not
18. resin, catalyst, catalyst
19. resin
20. frozen
21. shelf, may not
22. Glass microballoons
23. chopped fibers, flox
24. a. honeycomb
  b. foam
  c. wood
25. can
26. epoxy
27. Urethane
28. are
29. Pot, shelf
30. Material Safety Data Sheets
31. a. respirator
  b. goggles

c.   gloves
32.   fire, well ventilated
33.   a.   Methyl-Ethyl-Ketone
      b.   Acetone
34.   a.   Compression
           molding
      b.   Vacuum bagging
      c.   Filament winding
      d.   Wet lay-up
      e.   Fiberglass lay-up
35.   a.   Seal the surface.
      b.   Create a moisture an
           ultra-violet light
           barrier.
36.   a.   Aluminum wires
           woven into the top
           layer.
      b.   Aluminum screens
           under the top layer.
      c.   Aluminum foil
           bonded to the outer
           layer.
      d.   Aluminum flame
           sprayed onto the
           component.
37.   a.   Visual inspection
      b.   Tap testing
      c.   Ultrasonic testing
38.   tap test
39.   ultrasonic tester
40.   may
41.   Thermography
42.   Aramid
43.   backed up
44.   should not
45.   Carbide
46.   respirators
47.   Aramid
48.   should not
49.   cannot
50.   unairworthy
51.   a.   negligible
      b.   repairable
      c.   non-repairable
52.   routers
53.   Step sanding
54.   Scarf
55.   oil, grease
56.   warp clock
57.   a.   Remove excess resin
      b.   Compact the fiber
           layers
      c.   Remove trapped air
      d.   Maintain the original
           contour
      e.   Prevents shifting
58.   Vacuum bagging
59.   a.   Room temperature
           curing

b.   Heat curing.
60.   is not
61.   heating blankets
62.   Step
63.   Parting, release
64.   Bleeder materials
65.   should not
66.   potting
67.   potted
68.   delamination
69.   temporary, permanent
70.   balsa wood, composite
      honeycomb

SECTION 3C

1.   a.   Cellulose acetate base
      b.   Acrylic
2.   a.   Lucite
      b.   Plexiglas
3.   will not
4.   C
5.   crazed
6.   unsatisfactory
7.   a.   stretch forming
      b.   using male and
           female dies
      c.   vacuum forming
      d.   vacuum forming with
           female dies
8.   slowly, overheating
9.   150
10.   Ethylene dichloride
11.   does
12.   heat treating
13.   brass safety wire, screws,
      washers
14.   mild soap
15. $1/8^{th}$, expansion

CHAPTER
4

AIRCRAFT WELDING

SECTION 4A

1.   Fusion
2.   Adhesion
3.   a.   gas
      b.   electric arc
      c.   electrical resistance
4.   a.   oxygen
      b.   acetylene

5.   5,600 to 6,300
6.   infrared, ultraviolet, burn
7.   a.   arc welding helmet
      b.   gloves
      c.   proper clothing
8.   stick
9.   gas metal
10.   MIG
11.   tungsten inert gas, TIG
12.   tungsten
13.   11,000
14.   straight
15.   a.   spot
      b.   seam
16.   a.   current
      b.   pressure
      c.   dwell time
17.   a.   butt
      b.   tee
      c.   lap
      d.   corner
      e.   edge
18.   a.   uniform width
      b.   good penetration
      c.   adequate reinforcement
      d.   uniform ripples
19.   100
20.   capillary
21.   b
22.   tin, lead
23.   silver

SECTION 4B

1.   does not
2.   hydrogen
3.   cleaner
4.   carburizing
5.   inert gas
6.   oxygen, nitrogen
7.   DC
8. $1/10^{th}$, $1/4^{th}$
9.   lap
10.   scarf, fish-mouth
11.   heat treated, difficult,
      impossible

SECTION 4C

1.   15
2.   4 to 8
3.   acetone
4.   weight
5.   1/4, 1/2
6.   petroleum
7.   gasoline, alcohol,
      hydraulic, steam-cleaned
8.   close
9.   right

10. red, left
11. acetylene
12. green, right
13. equal pressure
14. tip
15. smaller
16. number drill
17. striker, matches/lighters
18. copper
19. will not
20. lighter
21. blue
22. thickness
23. neutral
24. neutral
25. acetylene

CHAPTER 5

AIRCRAFT FABRIC COVERING

SECTION 5A

1. aluminum
2. cellulose nitrate
3. is
4. a. Manufacturer's service manual
   b. Supplemental Type Certificate (STC)
   c. FAA field approval
5. 80
6. 56
7. Glider
8. a. Polyester
   b. Fiberglass
9. Reinforcing
10. Surface
11. second
12. cutting
13. Inspection grommets (rings)
14. Retarder
15. thinned
16. five
17. will not
18. plasticizers

SECTION 5B

1. 70
2. penetrate

3. a. Exposed to the sun
   b. Finished with dark colors
4. spar varnish
5. baseball
6. modified seine
7. a. blanket
   b. envelope
8. distilled or demineralized water
9. fungicidal
10. animal
11. loosen
12. 250
13. 1 4/5", 2 2/5"
14. beside
15. splice
16. grounded
17. 200
18. clear
19. much
20. glossy
21. Butyrate

SECTION 5C

1. sprayed
2. baseball, apex
3. four, eight, ten
4. sew

CHAPTER 6

AIRCRAFT PAINTING AND FINISHING

SECTION 6A

1. Plasticizers
2. Scotch-Brite
3. solvents, plasticizers
4. plasticizers
5. heavy
6. 20
7. too much
8. moisture
9. retarder
10. warming
11. a. Excessive heat or wind
    b. Excessively atomized spray gun air

12. a. Moving the gun too slowly.
    c. Holding the work too close.
    d. Not thinning the dope properly.
13. a. Improper spraying techniques.
    b. Thinners evaporating too quickly.
    c. Air drafts over the surface.
14. fisheyes
15. roping
16. a. They are designed for metal.
    b. They are more difficult to repair.
17. flexative modified primer
18. sandpaper

SECTION 6B

1. a. chemical
   b. mechanical
   c. pyrolytic
2. a. personal injury
   b. aircraft damage
3. Environmental Protection Agency (EPA), Occupational Health and Occupational Safety and Health Administration (OSHA)
4. a. aluminum tape (or foil)
   b. polyethylene sheeting
5. thick
6. hot water, steam
7. is not
8. plastic
9. polyurethane
10. conversion
11. a. zinc chromate
    b. epoxy
12. wash
13. a. primer
    b. acid
    c. thinner
14. 0.3 mil (0.0003in or 0.0076mm)
15. eight
16. moisture
17. low
18. B
19. polyurethane
20. Wash
21. induction
22. viscosity cup
23. 5, 24

24. pot
25. white reflective, transparent pigment, ultraviolet absorbing
26. polyurethane
27. will not
28. Linseed

SECTION 6C

1. heavier
2. daily
3. engine mounts, landing gear struts
4. suction, pressure
5. will not
6. air, electric
7. perpendicular
8. much
9. a. 2
   b. 5
   c. 1
   d. 3
   e. 4
10. True
11. 1/3 to 2/3
12. ahead of
13. thinner
14. polypropylene
15. 45
16. N
17. 58 inches
18. bad
19. water
20. wet

CHAPTER 7

AIRFRAME ELECTRICAL SYSTEMS

SECTION 7A

1. relative
2. strength, speed
3. a. direction of magnetic flux (north to south)
   b. direction of induced EMF (voltage)
   c. direction conductor moves through the magnetic field
4. armature
5. commutator
6. brushes
7. a. field frame
   b. armature
   c. commutator
   d. brush assembly
8. a. complete the magnetic circuit
   b. provide mechanical support for the other parts.
9. field, field poles, shoes
10. pigtail
11. carbon, commutator
12. a. series
    b. shunt
    c. compound
13. Series
14. flat, under, over
15. armature reaction
16. neutral
17. interpoles
18. coming-in, 1500
19. field
20. a. current limiter
    b. reverse current cutout (or relay)
    c. voltage regulator
21. reverse current
22. flashing (polarizing)
23. growler
24. large, light
25. stationary, moving
26. solid-state
27. a. rotor
    b. stator
    c. solid-state rectifier
    d. brush assembly
28. slip rings
29. replaced
30. is not
31. three
32. Y, delta
33. air, brushless
34. constant speed drive
35. 400, 3
36. lead-acid, nickel-cadmium
37. specific gravity
38. 1.275, 1.300
39. 1.150
40. hydrometer
41. 2.1
42. ampere-hours (amp-hours)
43. 5-hour discharge
44. clean, tight, corrosion
45. bristle brush, sodium bicarbonate (baking soda)
46. neutralizes
47. acid, water
48. current, voltage, voltage
49. a. carry most of the electrical loads
    b. charge the battery
50. 28, 14
51. baking soda, water
52. low
53. temperature
54. is not
55. chemically opposite, contaminate
56. boric acid, vinegar
57. fully charge or deep cycle, ampere-hour

SECTION 7B

1. relationship
2. voltage spikes
3. contactor
4. a. false
   b. false
   c. true
   d. true
5. coil
6. voltage
7. a. split-bus
   b. parallel-bus
8. parallel

SECTION 7C

1. 600
2. Eight
3. American Wire
4. a. 2 volts
   b. .5 volt
   c. 8 volts
   d. 7 volts
5. a. 4
   b. 2
   c. 10
   d. 2/0
6. 12, 15
7. 6, above
8. 25
9. shielding
10. a. red
    b. yellow
    c. blue
11. equal to
12. four
13. 3 milliohms (0.003 ohms)
14. co-axial
15. BNC

SECTION 7D

1. AC 43.13-1B
2. logical, consistent, up, forward
3. two, one
4. relay
5. slow-blow
6. trip-free
7. a. push-to-reset
   b. push-pull
   c. toggle type
8. a. red
   b. green
   c. white
9. a. rotating beacon
   b. flashing strobe
10. five
11. a. direction of the magnetic field
    b. direction of current flow
    c. direction the wire moves
12. a. permanent magnet
    b. electromagnet
13. a. series
    b. shunt
    c. compound
14. high
15. series
16. a. universal
    b. induction
    c. synchronous
17. a. the design
    b. the applied AC frequency

CHAPTER

8

HYDRAULIC AND PNEUMATIC POWER SYSTEMS

SECTION 8A

1. a. Lighter weight
   b. Ease of installation
   c. Simplified inspection
   d. Minimum maintenance
2. 100

3. incompressible
4. height of the column
5. equally, undiminished, all
6. pressure
7. F = AP (F = A x P)
8. V = AD (V = A x D)
9. a. Force can be easily transmitted over large distances.
   b. Large gains in mechanical advantage are possible.
10. a. 225 pounds (approx.)
    b. 2.25 inches (approx.)
    c. 445 pounds (approx.)
    d. 500 psi
11. a. up
    b. 1,570 pounds (approx.)

SECTION 8B

1. a. Able to flow with minimum opposition
   b. Must be incompressible
   c. Have good lubricating properties
   d. Inhibit corrosion
   e. Must not foam in operation.
2. Viscosity
3. flash point
4. a. Vegetable based
   b. Petroleum based
   c. Phosphate-ester based
5. is not
6. castor, alcohol
7. blue
8. MIL-H-5606
9. MIL-H-5606
10. fire
11. purple
12. soap, water
13. a. alcohol
    b. Stoddard solvent, naptha or varsol
    c. Trichlorethylene
14. a. natural rubber
    b. neoprene or Buna-N
    c. butyl rubber or ethylene-propylene elastomers

SECTION 8C

1. brakes
2. a. A suitable fluid
   b. A fluid reservoir

   c. A pump
   d. Actuators
3. power pack
4. a. Integral
   b. In-line
5. unpressurized
6. a. An aspirator in the return line.
   b. Bleed air
   c. Piston type
7. 0.000039
8. return
9. can
10. Double
11. constant
12. relief
13. constant
14. does not
15. flow
16. open
17. check
18. orifice check
19. sequence
20. Priority
21. hydraulic fuse
22. a. Pressure drop across the fuse
    b. Volume of fluid passing through the fuse
23. relief
24. pressure reducer
25. accumulator
26. air, nitrogen
27. a. piston type
    b. bladder type
    c. diaphragm type
28. H
29. linear
30. motor
31. one-way
32. two-way
33. larger
34. backup ring, 1500
35. cure
36. would
37. nicked, damaged

SECTION 8D

1. high
2. bleed
3. gyro instruments
4. Vane
5. dessicant, chemical dryer
6. shuttle
7. shuttle

CHAPTER 9

AIRCRAFT LANDING GEAR SYSTEMS

SECTION 9A

1. conventional
2. parasite
3. tricycle
4. ground loop, center of gravity
5. wheel pants
6. bungee
7. air-oil, oleo
8. oil
9. air
10. piston tube
11. two
12. aluminum, magnesium
13. bead seat
14. brake disk
15. fusible plugs
16. make sure it is completely deflated
17. deflator cap, valve, valve core
18. should not
19. should not
20. intergranular
21. overheating
22. is not
23. Eddy current
24. magnetic particle
25. any
26. shimmy damper
27. toed-in
28. negative
29. fire, damage
30. lowering
31. a. mechanical
    b. alternate hydraulic
    c. compressed air
    d. free-fall
32. squat
33. green, locked
34. retarded, any
35. is not, landing

SECTION 9B

1. sintered
2. main
3. deboosting (pressure-reducing)
4. lockout debooster
5. pneumatic
6. linings
7. 0.100
8. Spongy
9. bleeding
10. wheel cylinder
11. a. drain and flush the system
    b. replace all the seals
12. is not
13. fluorescent penetrant
14. is not
15. overheating
16. dragging

SECTION 9C

1. III (3)
2. width, diameter
3. outside diameter, width
4. does not
5. tubeless
6. more
7. bead
8. rib
9. nose
10. internally
11. under-inflated
12. Under-inflations
13. a. under-inflated
    b. over-inflated
    c. correct inflation
14. inflation pressure
15. airframe
16. cold
17. is
18. are
19. O-ring
20. cannot
21. is not
22. is
23. vertically
24. a. holes (punctures)
    b. defective valves
25. valve
26. light
27. anti-seize
28. talcum powder
29. heavy
30. slowly, safety cage
31. a. in special brackets
    b. with a cotter pin through holes in the rim
    c. with adhesive
32. Taxiing
33. stop, check the clearance
34. Hydroplaning

CHAPTER 10

POSITION AND WARNING SYSTEMS

SECTION 10A

1. blow, damage, control
2. zero
3. slip, skid
4. all the way
5. 20
6. weight, wheels (main wheels)
7. a. wheel-speed sensors
    b. anti-skid computer
    c. control valves
8. current, voltage
9. pressure, current
10. a. generate electrical signals usable by the control valve.
    b. regulate brake pressure to prevent a skid during landing
    c. prevent application of the brakes prior to touchdown.
11. locked-wheel
12. hydroplaning
13. test
14. wheel-speed sensor.

SECTION 10B

1. angle, attack
2. a. audible tone
    b. red light
3. stagnation point
4. stick-shaker
5. slot, vane
6. synchronous
7. permanent magnet
8. a. on the ground
    b. advanced for takeoff
9. green, red

10. landing, down, locked
11. reducing speed
12. Ground Proximity Warning System (GPWS)
13. Engine Indication, Crew Alerting
14. alert, status, maintenance

CHAPTER

AIRCRAFT INSTRUMENT SYSTEMS

SECTION 11A

1. a. absolute
    b. gauge
    c. differential
2. 29.92, 14.7
3. absolute
4. gauge
5. Bourdon
6. a. pitot
    b. static
7. absolute
8. engine pressure ratio
9. altimeter
10. indicated
11. mean sea level
12. inches, mercury (IIg), millibars
13. pressure
14. 32,000
15. temperature
16. is not
17. position
18. absolute, ground level
19. 91.411
20. 24
21. indicated
22. true
23. Machmeter
24. 0.95
25. vertical speed
26. static
27. Wheatstone bridge, ratiometer
28. thermocouple
29. is not
30. accelerometer (G-meter)
31. synchroscope

32. tachometer
33. a. rigidity in space
    b. precession
34. rigidity in space
35. a. pitch (lateral)
    b. roll (longitudinal)
36. vertical
37. precession
38. inclinometer
39. variation
40. isogonic
41. agonic
42. deviation
43. deviation
44. turning, acceleration
45. slaved
46. a. susceptible to icing
    b. produces no vacuum until the airplane is flying.
47. carbon
48. clean
49. cannot
50. a. airspeed and/or Mach indicator
    b. altimeter
    c. vertical speed
51. electric
52. static
53. resistor
54. one
55. two
56. air, fuel
57. pounds per square inch (psi)
58. most
59. a. Electronic Flight Instrument System
    b. Cathode Ray Tube
    c. Electronic Attitude Deviation Indicator
    d. Aeronautical Radio, Inc.
    e. Electronic Horizontal Situation Indicator
60. Zulu or Z

SECTION 11B

1. a. upper right
    b. upper center
    c. lower center
    d. upper left
2. low frequency, high amplitude
3. bonded, return
4. a. red radial line
    b. white arc
    c. yellow arc

    d. blue radial line
    e. green arc
5. removal
6. 100

CHAPTER

AIRCRAFT AVIONICS SYSTEMS

SECTION 12A

1. a. An electric field
    b. A magnetic field
2. shorter
3. oscillations, one
4. cycle, cycles, Hertz (Hz)
5. light
6. carrier, one-quarter, one-half
7. carrier, modulation
8. a. Amplitude Modulation (AM)
    b. Frequency Modulation (FM)
9. sky, long-range
10. a. generate a signal at the correct frequency
    b. modulate the carrier wave
    c. amplify the signal
11. oscillator
12. amplifier
13. shorter
14. Hertz dipole
15. ground plane
16. vertically
17. tuning
18. oceanic
19. VHF
20. is
21. UHF, voice, data
22. SELCAL
23. digital data link
24. airborne, ground
25. LF/MF
26. a. loop
    b. sense
27. VHF
28. phase
29. 30
30. is
31. direct to a destination
32. VORTAC

33. do not
34. acceleration
35. space
36. four
37. 4096
38. C
39. TCAS, resolve the potential conflict
40. 24
41. a. localizer
    b. glideslope
    c. marker beacons
    d. approach and runway lighting
42. UHF
43. glideslope
44. 75MHz
45. middle
46. 48, 121.5, 243.0
47. aft
48. rain
49. a. green
    b. yellow
    c. red
50. X-band
51. C-band
52. lightning discharges
53. transponders

SECTION 12B

1. manually control
2. ailerons
3. ailerons, elevators
4. pilot, throttle
5. Flight Management Systems
6. takeoff, landing, rollout
7. attitude, rate
8. servo
9. a. precess
   b. wear out
10. a. pneumatic
    b. electric
11. b.

SECTION 12C

1. bonding jumper
2. is
3. above, clamped
4. surge, spikes
5. snap-action
6. trip-free
7. 0.003
8. shielding
9. dischargers, wicks, trailing, atmosphere
10. Co-axial

11. dented, kinked, distorted, crushed, exposed

CHAPTER 13

AIRFRAME ICE AND RAIN CONTROL

SECTION 13A

1. known
2. anti-icing
3. deicing
4. spoiler
5. does not
6. bleed
7. bleed air
8. electrical heaters
9. alternate
10. electrically
11. heated
12. a. chemicals
    b. thermal (hot air)
    c. electrical heaters
13. a. carburetors
    b. propellers
    c. windshields
14. isopropyl
15. suction
16. vacuum
17. a. adhesives
    b. Rivnuts and screws
18. mild soap, water
19. electrothermal
20. slip-rings, brushes
21. on a sequenced cycle
22. holdover
23. takeoff, holdover
24. may not
25. ethylene glycol, isopropyl alcohol

SECTION 13B

1. a. mechanical wipers
   b. chemical rain repellant
   c. pneumatic rain-removal systems
2. a. electrically
   b. hydraulically.
3. is not
4. heavy

5. bleed

CHAPTER 14

CABIN ATMOSPHERE CONTROL SYSTEMS

SECTION 14A

1. a. 14.7
   b. 29.92
   c. 59
   d. 15
2. a. Nitrogen
   b. Oxygen
3. hypoxia
4. performance, judgment
5. Carbon monoxide
6. 10,000

SECTION 14B

1. will not
2. Aviator's Breathing
3. liquid
4. molecular sieve
5. green
6. a. DOT 3AA
   b. DOT 3HT
7. five-thirds, five
8. a. manual type
   b. automatic type
9. diluter-demand
10. continuous flow
11. continuous flow (rebreather)
12. stainless steel
13. LOX
14. 70
15. Sodium chlorate
16. does
17. long
18. cannot
19. opposite
20. 50, 100
21. lowest
22. 1725 p.s.i.
23. 50
24. allowed to leak out
25. engine turbochargers
26. a. cabin altitude
    b. cabin rate-of-climb (vertical speed)

c. differential pressure indicator
27. a. automatic
    b. manual
28. outflow

SECTION 14C

1. exhaust shroud
2. combustion
3. fuel valve
4. higher
5. fuel
6. C
7. a. ram air heat exchangers
    b. expanding air across a turbine
8. after
9. a. air-cycle machines vapor-cycle systems
10. latent
11. a. compressor
    b. expansion valve
12. receiver-dryer
13. dessicant
14. evaporator
15. R-12
16. control
17. condenser
18. a. soapy water
    b. electronic oscillator
19. sight glass
20. purged
21. vapor

CHAPTER

15

AIRCRAFT FUEL SYSTEMS

SECTION 15A

1. will
2. detonation, catastrophic failure
3. gasoline, kerosene
4. more
5. volatility
6. knock
7. lean
8. a. Avgas 80
    b. Avgas 100

c. Avgas 100LL
9. a. red
    b. green
    c. blue
10. a. Jet A
    b. Jet A-1
    c. Jet B
11. a. dissolved
    b. free
12. water
13. a. solids
    b. microorganisms
    c. surfactants
    d. water
    e. contamination caused by human error
14. is not
15. 150
16. 125
17. 2
18. jettison

SECTION 15B

1. cannot
2. a. Supply fuel pressure for starting
    b. Provide a backup for the engine-driven pump
    c. Assure fuel flow when switching tanks.
3. a. welded or riveted
    b. integral
    c. bladder
4. 3003, 5052
5. sloshing
6. integral
7. chafe-resisting
8. engine-oil
9. forward
10. 5052, stainless
11. sixth, third
12. lay
13. above
14. true
15. a. cone-type
    b. poppet-type
16. detent
17. a. electric motors
    b. solenoids
18. double
19. centrifugal
20. low
21. venturi
22. parallel
23. constant
24. series
25. a. bypass valve

b. relief valve
26. valve, plug
27. will not
28. capacitance
29. pressure

SECTION 15C

1. steam cleaning
2. 3.5
3. lead, tin
4. argon, carbon dioxide
5. one-half
6. 30
7. should not
8. is not
9. ground
10. a. Formation of sludge or slime.
    b. Emulsification of the fuel
    c. Creation of corrosive compounds and offensive odors.
11. Millipore
12. parallel
13. correct grade (type)

CHAPTER

16

FIRE PROTECTION SYSTEMS

SECTION 16A

1. a. Fuel
    b. Oxygen
    c. A source of ignition (heat)
2. a. C
    b. B
    c. D
    d. A
3. D
4. a. Spot-detection type
    b. Continuous-loop type
5. spot
6. pre-set
7. parallel
8. fault, short, open
9. spot-type
10. rate of temperature rise
11. reference

12. a. sensitive relay
     b. slave relay
13. continuous loop
14. Kidde
15. continuous loop
16. a. Lindberg
     b. Systron-Donner
17. a. Carbon Monoxide
     b. Nitrous Oxides
18. Ionization
19. a. The Light Refraction
         type
     b. The Ionization type
     c. The Solid-State type

SECTION 16B

1. is
2. five digit Halon
3. a. Weighing the
         container
     b. Checking the
         pressure gauge
4. squib
5. yellow
6. weighing
7. five
8. may not

CHAPTER

17

AIRCRAFT AIRWORTHINESS INSPECTION

SECTION 17A

1. airworthy
     a. aircraft specifications
     b. Type Certificate Data
         Sheets
     c. Airworthiness
         Directives
     d. Other FAA approved
         data
2. cycle
3. 43, D
4. a. Airworthiness
         Certificate
     b. Registration
         Certificate

     c. Weight and Balance
         information
     d. Operating
         Limitations(POH &
         Placards).
5. inoperative
6. 12 calendar
7. 100
8. midnight, May 31st
9. manufacturer
10. may not
11. discrepancies, unairworthy
12. major
13. special flight permit
14. 10
15. 1,427
16. may
17. Inspection Authorization
18. may not
19. Progressive
20. a. Large Airplanes (over
         12,500 lbs gross
         takeoff weight)
     b. Turbine powered
         multi-engine aircraft
21. conformity
22. 337
23. conformity
24. Continuous
25. letter
26. work cards
27. Approved
28. 24
29. special
30. 12
31. conditional

SECTION 17B

1. a. weather
     b. friction
     c. stress overloads
     d. heat
     e. vibration
2. weather
3. friction
4. stress
5. indirect
6. pre-inspection
7. work order
8. a. pre-inspection
     b. examination
     c. service and repair
     d. functional check
     e. return to service
9. mandatory
10. examination
11. functional
12. paperwork

13. appropriately rated

SECTION 17C

1. will
2. a. 43.9
     b. 43.11
3. a. A description of the
         work performed
     b. The date the work was
         completed
     c. The name of the person
         performing the work if
         different from the
         person approving the
         return to service.
     d. The signature of the
         person approving the
         return to service.
     e. The certificate number
         of the person
         approving the return to
         service.
     f. The type of certificate
         of the person
         approving the return to
         service.
4. owner
5. time in service
6. may